HERITAGE STUDIES

4

Activity Manual

Third Edition

bju press®

Greenville, South Carolina

Note
The fact that materials produced by other publishers may be referred to in this volume does not constitute an endorsement of the content or theological position of materials produced by such publishers. Any references and ancillary materials are listed as an aid to the student or the teacher and in an attempt to maintain the accepted academic standards of the publishing industry.

Heritage Studies 4 Activity Manual
Third Edition

Authors
Carol Arrington Ardt
Eileen Berry
Annittia Jackson
Ann Larson

Bible Integration
Brian C. Collins, PhD
Bryan Smith, PhD

Project Editors
Kaitlyn Chisholm
Maria S. Dixson

Page Layout
Bonnijean Marley

Project Coordinators
Michele White
Kendra Wright Winchester

Designer
Michael Asire

Cover Design
Elly Kalagayan

Cover Art
Ben Schipper

Cover Photography
Craig Oesterling

Illustrators
Preston Gravely
John Roberts
Lynda Slattery
Courtney Godbey Wise

Permissions
Sylvia Gass
Sarah Gundlach
Ashley Hobbs
Rita Mitchell
Carrie Walker

Photo credits appear on page 225.

ISBN 978-1-60682-729-1

15 14 13 12 11 10 9

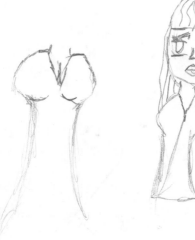

Contents

Dear Parent,

We are pleased to provide a comprehensive Heritage Studies program developed from the perspective of a Christian worldview. The Activity Manual accompanies the HERITAGE STUDIES 4 Student Text and is an integral part of the Heritage Studies 4 program.

The Activity Manual pages provide reinforcement of the skills taught in the Heritage Studies 4 materials and aid the teacher in evaluating each student's grasp of the concepts presented in the lessons. The pages include Bible connections, geography and map skill practice, study skills, and chapter reviews. Instructions for use of the Activity Manual are found in the HERITAGE STUDIES 4 Teacher's Edition.

As a parent there are many ways you can support and enhance your child's interest in and knowledge of history. Reading with your child is one vital way. The following trade book titles have been selected to correspond to your child's grade level and social studies themes in these materials. These titles are available at JourneyForth Books, a division of BJU Press. Visit journeyforth.com to place an order.

JourneyForth Titles

Brave the Wild Trail by Milly Howard

Prairie Anna by Peggy House

Carolina's Courage by Elizabeth Yates

Tales from Dust River Gulch by Tim Davis

Pelts and Promises by Nancy Lohr

Peanut Butter Friends in a Chop Suey World by Deb Brammer

Ira Sankey: Singing the Gospel by Kelly Bruss

Pollyanna by Eleanor H. Porter

Understood Betsy by Dorothy Canfield Fisher

The Lost Prince of Samavia by Frances Hodgson Burnett

A Father's Promise by Donnalyn Hess

Cause and Effect

Match each *cause* with its *effect*.

Cause

_____ 1. Because some important people in Europe said that the Bible was not God's Word . . .

_____ 2. Because the Pilgrims and Puritans wanted to follow the Bible in their worship of God . . .

_____ 3. Because the Holy Spirit worked in people's hearts . . .

_____ 4. Because both the British and the French claimed the same land . . .

_____ 5. Because the American colonists had done much of the fighting and did not get to vote on British laws . . .

_____ 6. Because the First Continental Congress wanted Britain to correct the wrongs being done to them . . .

_____ 7. Because General Washington did not seize power after the Revolutionary War . . .

_____ 8. Because George Washington was a just ruler . . .

Effect

A. the French and Indian War started.

B. they traveled to the New World to live.

C. they sent a letter to the British king.

D. Americans trusted him and elected him to be president for two terms.

E. many people trusted Christ to be their Savior.

F. he was a great blessing to his nation.

G. false ideas began spreading to the American colonies.

H. they thought paying taxes to Britain was unjust.

Identifying the cause and effect of an event enables you to understand why that event happened.

Write the names of each continent, ocean, and hemisphere.

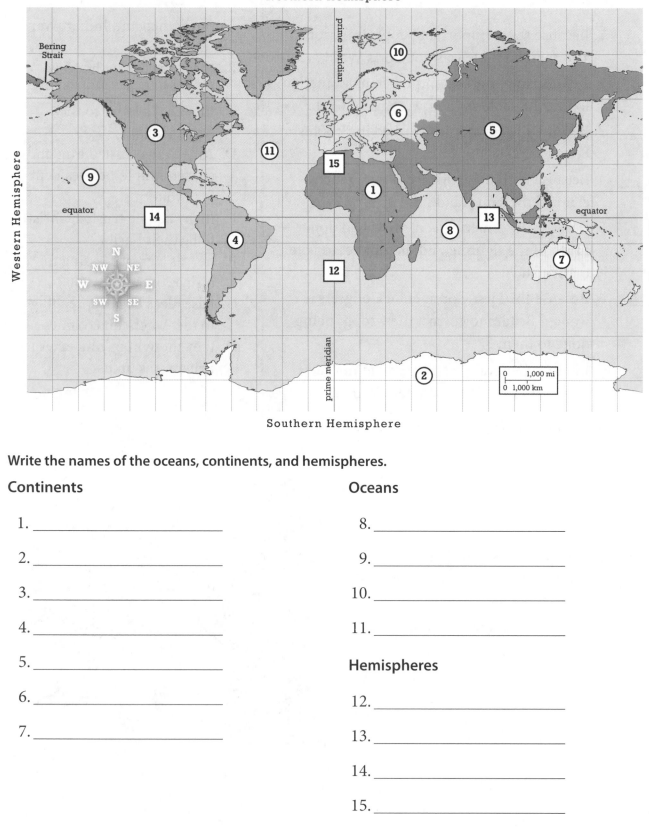

Write the names of the oceans, continents, and hemispheres.

Continents

1. _____

2. _____

3. _____

4. _____

5. _____

6. _____

7. _____

Oceans

8. _____

9. _____

10. _____

11. _____

Hemispheres

12. _____

13. _____

14. _____

15. _____

Robert E. Lee was the leader for the Confederate army. Ulysses S. Grant was the leader for the Union army. The two leaders met on April 9, 1865, at a town called Appomattox Court House in Virginia. At the McLean farmhouse they agreed on the terms of surrender. The war between the states was over. Grant allowed the Southern soldiers to keep their guns and horses. The Confederate soldiers signed pledges to not take up arms again. Grant gave them enough provisions to get home.

Complete the puzzle.

ACROSS

1. state where Appomattox Court House is located
3. farmhouse where Lee and Grant met
7. another name for the Northern army
9. what the Confederate soldiers signed to not take up arms again
10. what Grant gave the Confederate soldiers
11. leader of the Confederate army (last name)

DOWN

2. leader of the Union army (last name)
4. another name for the Southern army
5. the terms Lee and Grant agreed on
6. town where the agreement for surrender was signed (first part)
8. the month Lee and Grant met to sign an agreement

McLean House

Rebuilding the Nation

Use the glossary to define the terms.

1. Reconstruction _____

   _____

   _____

2. freedmen _____

   _____

3. industry _____

   _____

Carpenters' docks in Chicago, late 1800s

List some responses of the Northerners, Southerners, and freedmen to the Reconstruction.

Northerners	Southerners	Freedmen

Draw a picture showing something you have learned about in this chapter.
Draw it in the style Thomas Nast used for his political cartoons.

Rebuilding to Reunite

Circle the Northern soldier if the description applies to the Northerners.
Circle the Southern soldier if the description applies to the Southerners.
Circle the freedman if the description applies to the freedmen.

1. became less interested in changing the South

2. had state governments controlled by Democrats

3. wanted to be independent

4. wanted to be treated fairly and own their own land

5. wanted to govern their own states again

6. hoped their land would be restored to how it was before the war

7. wanted to make sure the Civil War was not in vain

8. wanted to make sure the freedmen were treated fairly

9. were too busy worrying about work and business to keep helping the South

10. were treated as less important than others

11. lost their protection when Northern troops left the South

12. gained railroads and industry

Ally

The Golden Spike National Historic Site can be visited to see where the Central Pacific and the Union Pacific railroads met. The workers drove the last spike into the track that connected the East to the West. Communication and travel became easier, faster, and cheaper because of the transcontinental railroad.

Use the key to draw lines for the transcontinental railroad.

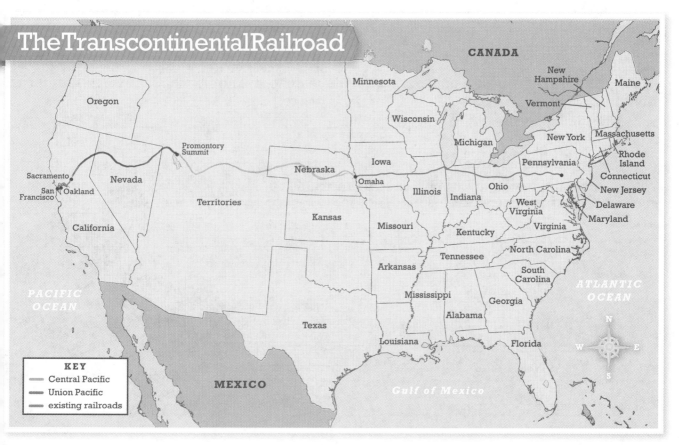

The Transcontinental Railroad

KEY
— Central Pacific
— Union Pacific
— existing railroads

The Golden Rule

In Matthew 7:12 Jesus teaches about kindness. Many Irish and Chinese immigrants were treated unkindly. Jesus wants people to be kind to everyone.

Read and answer the questions.

1. At a friend's birthday party, there is only one slice of cheese pizza left. You and your friend both want another slice of cheese pizza. What should you do? _____

_____

2. A new child spills his drink at a get-together. Other children laugh at the accident. What should you do? _____

3. Someone calls you a mean name. What should you do? _____

_____

_____

4. A friend trips and falls. Other friends laugh. What should you do? _____

_____

5. It is your turn to choose a song to sing in Sunday school. Another child thinks it is his turn. What should you do? _____

_____

Write about when someone was unkind to you. Include how you would have liked the person to respond.

_____

_____

_____

_____

_____

_____

Homesteaders

Write *True* if the statement is true.
If the statement is false, write the correction for the underlined word.

_____ 1. The important act that opened land in the West to settlers was called the <u>Sodbusters</u> Act.

_____ 2. The act allowed settlers to own 160 acres if they built a house, lived on the land, and improved the land over a period of <u>five</u> years.

_____ 3. Prairie farmers who raised corn, wheat, cattle, and hogs were called <u>sodbusters</u>.

_____ 4. The Great Plains became known as <u>"America's Breadbasket"</u> because of farmers growing wheat.

_____ 5. Joseph Glidden invented <u>the windmill</u>.

Pioneer family photographed outside their sod house in Nebraska, 1886

Write the correct word to complete the sentence.

_____ 6. Among the people who flocked to claim land in the West were ____, single women, and widows.

_____ 7. Immigrants from Russia brought Turkey Red ____ to America's Great Plains.

_____ 8. Homesteaders built their homes out of ____.

_____ 9. Since very little rain fell on the plains, many farmers used a ____ to pump water.

_____ 10. One challenge sodbusters faced were swarms of ____ that destroyed their crops.

Postcard Activity

Draw a picture to illustrate an experience that may have occurred during the Oklahoma Land Rush.

Write about the experience to a family member or friend.

The Bill of Rights

1. Congress cannot make an official national religion or stop you from practicing your religion. Congress cannot stop you from meeting peacefully to ask the government to change something.

2. Congress cannot stop you from having and carrying weapons.

3. You do not have to let soldiers live in your house, except if there is a war, and only if Congress has passed a law about it.

4. Nobody can search you, your house, or your papers unless he can prove to a judge that he has a good reason to think you are guilty of a crime.

5. You cannot be tried for any serious crime without a grand jury meeting first to decide whether there is enough support for a trial. And if the jury decides you are innocent, the government cannot try again. You don't have to say anything at your trial. You can't be killed, put in jail, or fined unless you are convicted of a crime by a jury. And the government can't take anything that is yours, unless the government pays for it.

6. If you are arrested, you have a right to a quick trial, and the government cannot keep you in jail without trying you. The trial has to be public, so everyone knows what is happening. The case has to be decided by a jury of people from your area. You have the right to know what you are accused of, to see and hear the people who are witnesses against you, and to have the government help you get witnesses on your side. You also have the right to have a lawyer help you.

7. You have the right to a jury when it is a law case between two people.

8. The government cannot make you pay more than is reasonable in bail or in fines, and the government cannot order you to be tortured.

9. Just because these rights are listed in the Constitution does not mean that you do not have other rights too.

10. Anything that the Constitution does not say that Congress can do should be left up to the states or to the people.

Complete the Venn Diagram using Activity Manual pages 33 and 209.
Write three ways the Bill of Rights and Chief Joseph's requests are different.
Write three ways they are the same.

Chief Joseph's Requests

How They Are the Same

Bill of Rights

HERITAGE STUDIES

Historic Site

Coney Island was America's first amusement park. Over time it became a large park with rides, games, and sideshows. It had the first roller coaster in America. The first hot dogs in America were sold at Coney Island. This amusement park is still enjoyed today.

Design and name a ride for an amusement park.

Name of ride _____

Immigrants

Match the words to the correct definition.

_____ 1. Ellis Island

_____ 2. Statue of Liberty

_____ 3. Gilded Age

_____ 4. Chinese Exclusion Act

A. reminder for new immigrants of the freedom they hoped to find in a new land
B. a law that said no more Chinese from the working class could enter America
C. location of the first immigrant station
D. description of American culture in the late 1800s

Mark all the correct answers. A question may have more than one correct answer.

5. Why did immigrants come to the United States during the Gilded Age?
   - ○ to find land for sale at a good price
   - ○ to look for good jobs
   - ○ to visit
   - ○ to escape famine

6. What did many immigrants need when they first arrived in America?
   - ○ doctors
   - ○ help with learning English
   - ○ help finding relatives already living in America
   - ○ new luggage

Describe the Chinese immigrants.

_____

_____

_____

_____

_____

_____

Inventions

Write *AGB* if the photo applies to Alexander Graham Bell.
Write *TE* if the photo applies to Thomas Edison.
Write *JM* if the photo applies to Jan Matzeliger.
Write *CS* if the photo applies to Christopher Sholes.

_____ 1.

_____ 2.

_____ 3.

_____ 4.

_____ 5.

Match the description with the correct person.

_____ 6. teacher for the deaf in Boston

_____ 7. worker in an American shoe factory

_____ 8. gun company produced his invention

_____ 9. inventor of a machine that recorded the human voice and played it back

_____ 10. inventor of the QWERTY keyboard

> A. Alexander Graham Bell
> B. Thomas Edison
> C. Jan Matzeliger
> D. Christopher Sholes

Explain how inventions changed the way people lived.

_____

_____

_____

Rags to Riches

Circle the *train* if the statement applies to Vanderbilt.
Circle the *steel beam* if the statement applies to Carnegie.
Circle the *oil can* if the statement applies to Rockefeller.

1. earned a fortune in the steel business

2. became rich through the railroad and through shipping

3. earned his wealth in the oil industry

4. gave much of his money to build libraries

5. gave much of his money to medical research

Explain how capitalism works.

_____

_____

_____

_____

Explain what God expects people to do whether they have money or not.

_____

_____

_____

_____

_____

Answer the questions.

1. Who was the first immigrant to be received at the new station in New York Harbor?

   _____

2. Who invented the first modern typewriter? _____

3. Who invented the first telephone? _____

4. Who invented the phonograph? _____

5. Who invented the shoe laster? _____

6. Who became rich through the railroad and through shipping? _____

7. Who earned his fortune in the steel business? _____

8. Who earned his wealth in the oil industry? _____

Match the description with the correct word.

_____ 9. description of American culture in the late 1800s

_____ 10. the immigrant station in New York Harbor

_____ 11. a law that said no more Chinese from the working class could enter America

_____ 12. a system of government in which the people of a country own the country's goods and businesses

> A. capitalism
> B. Chinese Exclusion Act
> C. Ellis Island
> D. Gilded Age

*Breezing Up
(A Fair Wind)*
by Winslow Homer

Complete the chart.

Louisa May Alcott	wrote _____
Mary Cassatt	painted mothers and _____
Emily Dickinson	wrote _____
Antonin Dvořák	composed _____
William Randolph Hearst	owned a _____
Winslow Homer	painted _____ from everyday life
Scott Joplin	wrote ragtime _____
Edward MacDowell	wrote classical _____ music
Joseph Pulitzer	owned a _____
John Singer Sargent	painted _____
John Philip Sousa	wrote _____
Louis Tiffany	made _____-glass objects
Mark Twain	wrote _____

Mark the correct answer.

1. Which type of theater made up of short acts became popular during the Gilded Age?
   - ○ opera
   - ○ circus
   - ○ vaudeville
   - ○ sporting events

2. What traveling show about life in the West became a popular event?
   - ○ Annie Oakley's Vaudeville
   - ○ Buffalo Bill's Wild West Show
   - ○ Buffalo Bill's Vaudeville
   - ○ Annie Oakley's Wild West Show

William F. Cody

3. What was Annie Oakley an expert at?
   - ○ shooting guns ○ riding horses ○ roping cows ○ throwing knives

4. What was the name of the first amusement park near New York City?
   - ○ New York City Amusement Park ○ Coney Island
   - ○ Wild West in New York ○ Coney Island's Wild West

5. What ride was first introduced at New York's first amusement park?
   - ○ carousel ○ bumper cars ○ Ferris wheel ○ roller coaster

6. What food item was first made and sold at New York's first amusement park?
   - ○ funnel cakes ○ hot dogs ○ onion rings ○ french fries

7. What sporting event became popular to watch during the Gilded Age?
   - ○ boxing ○ hockey ○ cricket ○ golf

8. What became common during this time that was both fun and a healthy way to exercise?
   - ○ swimming ○ fishing ○ bicycling ○ golfing

9. What did women wear so their long skirts would not get caught in the bike chain?
   - ○ bloomers ○ pants ○ split skirt ○ overalls

Explain what A. C. Dixon warned about amusement parks.

_____

_____

_____

Write *JA* if the statement applies to Jane Addams.
Write *SA* if the statement applies to Elizabeth Stanton and Susan B. Anthony.

_____ 1. formed a plan to help immigrants in poor living conditions

_____ 2. spoke out openly for women's rights

_____ 3. started Hull-House for immigrant women

_____ 4. rejected verses in God's Word about women

Write the correct word to complete the sentence.

> pasteurization   settlement houses   suffrage

Jane Addams

_____ 5. The need for women's ____ was slowly becoming more accepted.

_____ 6. The special treatment that milk needed before being sold was called ____.

_____ 7. Places for poor immigrants to go for help were called ____.

Mark all the correct answers.

8. What did Hull-House provide immigrants?
   ○ food and clothing   ○ jobs   ○ classes   ○ childcare

9. What laws did labor unions and reform workers want for child labor?
   ○ limits on the number of hours a child could work
   ○ decision on what age a child could begin working
   ○ limits on how long breaks should be
   ○ decision on how much education children must have before they can work

Explain how life for women in America changed during the Gilded Age.

_____

_____

Explain how pasteurization works.

_____

_____

Family History Activity

Follow the directions.

1. Choose an older person in your family to interview.

2. Look at photos, letters, diaries, or scrapbooks to gather information about your family.

3. Find out if any family member came from another country.

4. Make a family tree.

5. Write an interesting or funny story from your family's past.

6. Share your story with the class.

Use these questions to interview your family member.

1. What is your full name and why did your parents select this name for you?
2. What do you know about your family name?
3. When and where were you born?
4. How did your family come to live in America?
5. Are there other family members in this area? What are their names?
6. What is your earliest childhood memory?
7. What kind of games did you play growing up?
8. What was your favorite toy and why?
9. Did you have family chores?
10. What was school like for you as a child?
11. What school activities and sports did you participate in?
12. Did you have any pets?
13. What world events had the most impact on you while you were growing up?
14. How were holidays celebrated in your family?
15. Did your family have any special traditions?
16. How is the world today different from what it was like when you were a child?
17. What is a family story that has been passed down through the generations?
18. Are there any stories about famous or infamous relatives in your family?
19. Are there any physical characteristics that run in your family?
20. Are there any special heirlooms, photos, recipes, Bibles, or other keepsakes that have been passed down in your family?
21. What did your family enjoy doing together?
22. What did you learn from your parents that was most valuable?
23. What accomplishments are you the most proud of?

Write *M* if the statement applies to D. L. Moody.
Write *S* if the statement applies to Ira Sankey.

_____ 1. worked in his uncle's shoe store in Boston

_____ 2. was a singer and composer

_____ 3. became a Christian when his Sunday school
teacher spoke with him about Christ

_____ 4. started a Sunday school

_____ 5. wrote over 1,000 gospel songs

_____ 6. was invited to preach in London

_____ 7. used business methods to get the word out about his meetings

_____ 8. wrote music for "The Ninety and Nine"

_____ 9. helped prepare people to hear God's Word

_____ 10. received a response to his preaching much like the Great Awakening in the 1700s

Explain the falsehood concerning faith that developed during the Gilded Age.

_____

_____

_____

_____

_____

Write the answer that completes each sentence.

| capitalism | Ellis Island | portrait | Statue of Liberty |
| Chinese Exclusion Act | Gilded Age | ragtime | |

_____ 1. The term that is used to describe American culture in the late 1800s is the ____.

_____ 2. A system that allows the people of a country to own the country's goods and businesses is called ____.

_____ 3. A new form of music that became popular at the end of the 1800s is called ____.

_____ 4. The law that said no more Chinese from the working class could enter America was called the ____.

_____ 5. The gift from France that reminded new immigrants of freedom is the ____.

_____ 6. A painting of a person that became a popular form of art during the Gilded Age is called a ____.

_____ 7. The station the US government set up to provide help for immigrants is called ____.

Write *True* if the statement is true.
If the statement is false, write the correction for the underlined word.

_____ 8. The telephone could <u>pasteurize</u> the human voice over wires.

_____ 9. The first machine to record the human voice and play it back was the <u>QWERTY keyboard</u>.

_____ 10. During the Gilded Age some of the greatest American poetry was written by <u>Emily Dickinson</u>.

_____ 11. A type of theater that became popular during the Gilded Age was a show made up of short acts called <u>the circus</u>.

_____ 12. During the Gilded Age the need for women's <u>suffrage</u> became more accepted.

Mark the correct answer.

13. Who invented the first telephone?
    - ○ Christopher Sholes
    - ○ Jan Matzeliger
    - ○ Alexander Graham Bell
    - ○ Thomas Edison

14. Who invented the phonograph?
    - ○ Christopher Sholes
    - ○ Jan Matzeliger
    - ○ Alexander Graham Bell
    - ○ Thomas Edison

15. Who became rich through the railroad and through shipping?
    - ○ Cornelius Vanderbilt
    - ○ Jan Matzeliger
    - ○ Andrew Carnegie
    - ○ John D. Rockefeller

16. Who earned his wealth in the oil industry?
    - ○ Cornelius Vanderbilt
    - ○ Jan Matzeliger
    - ○ Andrew Carnegie
    - ○ John D. Rockefeller

17. Who earned a fortune in the steel business?
    - ○ Cornelius Vanderbilt
    - ○ Jan Matzeliger
    - ○ Andrew Carnegie
    - ○ John D. Rockefeller

18. Who started a settlement house for immigrant women to receive help?
    - ○ Elizabeth Cady Stanton
    - ○ Jane Addams
    - ○ Annie Oakley
    - ○ Susan B. Anthony

19. Which man did God use to win thousands of people to Christ during the Gilded Age?
    - ○ D. L. Moody
    - ○ Christopher Sholes
    - ○ William Cody
    - ○ Joseph Pulitzer

Explain how the new labor laws improved the lives of children.

_____

_____

_____

_____

On February 15, 1898, an American warship mysteriously blew up. The sinking of the USS *Maine* sparked a war between the United States and Spain. The *Maine* was anchored in Havana, Cuba. Spain was mistreating the Cubans. The United States and other nations tried to help the Cubans. When the *Maine* sank, President McKinley and Congress decided to use force. They wanted to set up a stable government and secure Cuba's independence. The Spanish-American War lasted 100 days. The United States won every battle that was fought. The Spanish signed a treaty to give up control of Cuba and other small countries in the Pacific.

Today there is a memorial located at Arlington National Cemetery where most of the sailors who died on the *Maine* are buried. The memorial includes the mainmast of the *Maine*.

Write a newspaper article about the sinking of the USS *Maine*.

_____

_____

_____

_____

_____

_____

_____

_____

_____

_____

_____

From Sea to Shining Sea

Label the oceans.
Label the countries in the key to match the map.

OCEAN

OCEAN

OCEAN

N
W · E
S

City Map

A city map shows places of interest and streets in a city. Shapes on this map and key identify public parking and metro stations. A map scale is used to measure the distance between places of interest.

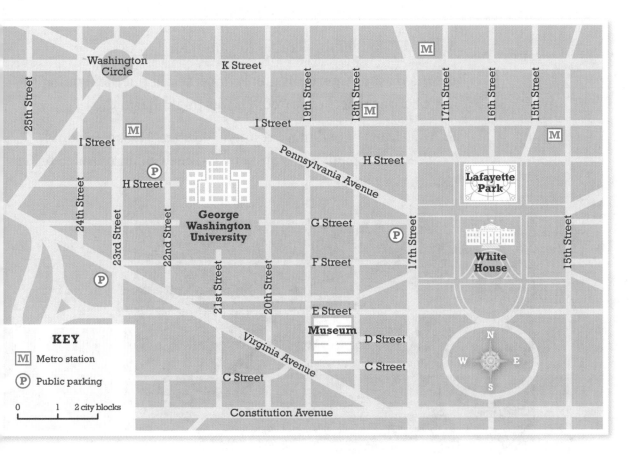

Answer the questions.

1. How are the streets named that run north to south? _____

2. How are the streets named that run east to west? _____

3. How many metro stations are there? _____

4. How many parking areas are there? _____

5. How many city blocks of **I Street** are shown on this map? _____

6. What route would be the shortest if you were at Washington Circle and wanted to go to the

   White House? _____

Cuba's Independence

Write the answer that completes each sentence.

_____ 1. Cuba was the most important island in the ____.

_____ 2. The country that claimed Cuba was ____.

_____ 3. Cubans fought three times to gain their ____.

_____ 4. One reason Americans grew concerned about the fighting in Cuba was that they feared the war might harm their ____.

_____ 5. Americans hoped that President William McKinley could talk to the Spanish government and the Cuban rebels to bring about ____.

Write _True_ if the statement is true.
If the statement is false, write the correction for the underlined word.

_____ 6. Columbus discovered Spain.

_____ 7. The war between Spain and Cuba destroyed many sugarcane fields.

_____ 8. Americans heard that the Spanish forced Cubans to live in prisons.

_____ 9. Most Americans in the 1890s were Catholic.

_____ 10. A few Americans wanted to make Cuba a colony.

_____

Write the answer that completes each sentence.

_____ 1. The idea that America should spread from one ocean to another was called ____.

_____ 2. The United States stopped expanding after ____.

_____ 3. The very cold land in the northwestern tip of North America that was bought from Russia is ____.

_____ 4. Some people wanted to control foreign lands by practicing ____.

_____ 5. One of the biggest problems for steamships was getting ____.

_____ 6. Lines on a map that run up and down are called lines of ____.

_____ 7. Lines on a map that run from side to side are called lines of ____.

_____ 8. The most important island in the Caribbean was ____.

_____ 9. The item that Cuba exported to the United States but that was being destroyed by the war was ____.

_____ 10. Some countries wanted to build a ____ as a shortcut throught Central America.

**Write *True* if the statement is true.
If the statement is false, write the correction for the underlined word(s).**

_____ 11. From the earliest days, Americans viewed their <u>resources</u> as something special.

_____ 12. One man who believed America should grow was <u>William Seward</u>, who purchased Alaska.

_____ 13. After the Civil War, traveling around the world became easier because many ships had <u>steam engines</u>.

_____ 14. A line that compares distances on the map to distances in the real world is called a <u>compass rose</u>.

Mark all the correct answers.

15. Why did the United States and the Confederate States not try to expand during the Civil War?
    - ○ They were not interested in claiming new lands.
    - ○ They did not have enough money.
    - ○ They were too busy fighting.
    - ○ They did not want to spread the American way of life around the world.

16. Why did many Americans side with the Cubans against Spain?
    - ○ Americans wanted the gold from the land.
    - ○ Americans remembered their own country's fight for freedom from England.
    - ○ Americans did not like to see other humans beings treated without care.
    - ○ Americans wanted the rich fishing grounds.

Complete the section.

17. List the areas of North America into which America spread. _____

_____

18. Explain how the purchase of Alaska was a wise choice. _____

_____

_____

19. Write two reasons why President Grant wanted the Caribbean Islands to be part of the

United States. _____

_____

_____

20. Explain why Americans wanted to expand. _____

_____

_____

_____

21. List features that are found on most maps. _____

Blockade

Number the events in the order that they occurred.

_____ 1. The Spanish ambassador wrote a letter to his friend in Cuba that spoke rudely of President McKinley.

_____ 2. The Spanish-American War began.

_____ 3. Senator Proctor visited Cuba and spoke to the Senate, listing all the bad things he had seen in Cuba.

_____ 4. The USS _Maine_ blew up in the harbor of Havana, Cuba.

_____ 5. The US Navy began a blockade of Cuba.

_____ 6. Congress passed a law that Americans should not give military aid to the Cubans.

_____ 7. Newspapers across America published the de Lôme letter.

Explain how yellow journalism worked.

_____

_____

_____

_____

_____

_____

_____

_____

_____

_____

Military Branches

The United States military protects America and keeps its citizens safe. America's military has five branches. The Army, Marine Corps, Navy, Air Force, and Coast Guard are headed by the commander in chief, the president. The Army's job is to protect and defend the security and resources of the United States. The Army provides ground troops. The Marine Corps works from Navy craft at sea and is first at the scene of a conflict. The Navy protects America's interests at home and around the world. The Air Force protects the United States from the air as well as space and cyberspace. The Coast Guard serves by protecting the nation's waterways. Each branch of the United States military works together to protect our nation.

Write several sentences about a family member or someone you know who is serving or has served in the US military. Include which branch the person served in and how and when that person served.

_____

_____

_____

_____

_____

_____

_____

Map Grid

Complete the section.

1. Use the map on page 143 in your textbook to label the bodies of water on the map.

2. What two battles were fought at C2?

   _____ and _____

3. What is the location of Cuba's capital? _____

4. What small, Spanish-owned island is located at F2? _____

5. About how far is Havana from Santiago de Cuba? _____

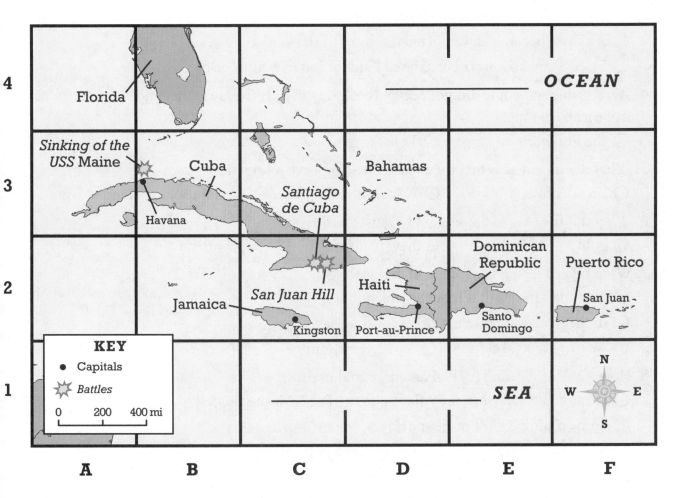

Aftermath

Mark all the correct answers.

1. Why did American and Spanish officials meet in Paris, France?
   - ○ to decide who had won the war
   - ○ to fight their final battle
   - ○ to work out a peace treaty

2. Which lands did Spain give up?
   - ○ Guam
   - ○ France
   - ○ Cuba

Panama Canal

3. What change in world powers did the Treaty of Paris show?
   - ○ Spain was no longer considered a major force in the world.
   - ○ America became an important country in the world.
   - ○ France was no longer considered a major force in the world.

4. What group of people did not accept the Treaty of Paris because they did not want to be an American colony?
   - ○ the Philippines
   - ○ France
   - ○ Cuba

5. What document says that the Senate must approve all treaties?
   - ○ Treaty of Paris
   - ○ Constitution
   - ○ Declaration of Independence

6. What did the United States gain because of the war?
   - ○ gold
   - ○ new lands
   - ○ power

7. What helped lessen the spread of disease?
   - ○ burning candles that repelled mosquitoes
   - ○ draining wet areas to get rid of mosquitoes
   - ○ wearing special clothes that repelled mosquitoes

8. How was the building of the Panama Canal useful?
   - ○ Ships could sail from the Atlantic to the Pacific more quickly.
   - ○ Ships could be built more quickly.
   - ○ Ships faced fewer storms by going through the canal.

9. Who discovered how yellow fever spread?
   - ○ Andrew Carnegie
   - ○ Walter Reed
   - ○ Grover Cleveland

Define each term.

1. ambassador _____

2. imperialism _____

3. journalism _____

Write the answer that completes each sentence.

_____ 4. From the earliest days, Americans viewed their ____ as something special.

_____ 5. After the Civil War, traveling around the world became easier because many ships had ____.

_____ 6. A line that compares distance on a map to distances in the real world is a ____.

_____ 7. Cuba fought Spain three different times to gain its ____.

_____ 8. One of the events that made Americans upset with Spain was the ____ letter.

_____ 9. The explosion of the ____ on February 15 was a great mystery.

_____ 10. To keep the Spanish ships from leaving the Cuban harbor, the US ships set up a ____.

Write *True* if the statement is true.
If the statement is false, write the correction for the underlined word(s).

_____ 11. The idea that America should spread from one ocean to another is called <u>Manifest Destiny</u>.

_____ 12. One of the biggest problems for steamships was getting <u>wood</u>.

_____ 13. Lines on a map that run up and down are called lines of <u>latitude</u>.

_____ 14. American and Spanish officials met in Paris, France, to sign the <u>Treaty of Paris</u>.

Match the description with the person.

_____ 15. William Seward

_____ 16. President Grant

_____ 17. President McKinley

_____ 18. Enrique Dupuy de Lôme

_____ 19. Walter Reed

_____ 20. Theodore Roosevelt

A. wrote a letter to his friend in Cuba that spoke rudely of President McKinley
B. wanted to help Spain and Cuba make peace
C. helped lead the Rough Riders in the Battle of San Juan Hill
D. wanted to add Santo Domingo to the United States to put a naval base there
E. bought Alaska from Russia
F. proved that mosquitoes spread yellow fever

Mark all the correct answers.

21. Into what areas did America spread before 1853?
   ○ Canada
   ○ Texas
   ○ Oregon Country
   ○ Cuba

22. Why did Americans want to expand beyond North America?
   ○ to tell more people around the world about Jesus
   ○ to make money
   ○ to claim more land like other countries
   ○ to spread the American way of life around the world

23. Who is the commander in chief of the military?
   ○ any government official
   ○ the president of the United States
   ○ all members of Congress
   ○ a top military officer appointed by the president

24. What lands did America take over because of the war in Cuba?
   ○ the Philippines
   ○ France
   ○ Hawaii
   ○ Puerto Rico

Read the article and complete the fact sheet.

In 1903 Wilbur and Orville Wright made the first airplane flights at Kitty Hawk, North Carolina. Congress approved the building of Kill Devil Hills Monument National Memorial on March 2, 1927. It was made to honor the first flight of a powered aircraft carrying a man who controlled the plane.

On August 10, 1933, the War Department turned the land over to the National Park Service, US Department of the Interior. It was renamed the Wright Brothers National Memorial on December 1, 1953. The majority of glider tests were done at this location as well as the first four airplane flights. A granite monument with the names of Wilbur and Orville Wright stands 60 feet tall at the memorial. This historic site includes about 425 acres.

Wright Brothers National Memorial

Historic site's original name _____

Approved by _____

Date approved _____

Honors the _____

_____

Land turned over to the _____

New name _____

Date renamed _____

Location _____

Monument facts _____

Size of historic site _____

Progress and Problems

Write *1800* if the statement refers to the year 1800.
Write *1900* if the statement refers to 1900.

_____ 1. New inventions made life better.

_____ 2. The United States had more wealth than any other nation in the world.

_____ 3. The Mississippi River formed the western border of the United States.

_____ 4. Americans lived longer than ever.

_____ 5. Americans imported most manufactured goods.

_____ 6. Foreign navies stopped American ships as they sailed on the seas.

_____ 7. Medicine improved.

_____ 8. The United States was not one of the powerful nations of the world.

_____ 9. Americans had more free time to enjoy sports, concerts, and other activities.

_____ 10. Nations around the world imported American goods.

Write *B* if the statement refers to problems with *business*,
***P* if the statement refers to problems related to the *poor*,**
or *F* if the statement refers to problems related to *farmers*.

_____ 11. Some moved to work in mines or factories.

_____ 12. Sometimes workers would go on strike.

_____ 13. The leaders became much wealthier than anyone else in the country.

_____ 14. The tenements were bad places to live.

_____ 15. At times the conflicts between the strikers and the guards became violent.

_____ 16. They wanted more power returned to the ordinary people.

_____ 17. They might not practice the skills needed to get good jobs.

Answer the questions.

_____ 18. What word described American life in the early 1900s?

_____ 19. Who made people aware of problems in America?

_____ 20. Who wrote news stories that focused on bad news and sin?

HERITAGE STUDIES

Think on These Things

Muckraker journalists often stretched the truth when writing news stories that focused on bad news and sin. Read Philippians 4:8 in the Bible to learn what God wants us to think about.

Write an article about a recent church event or something that happened in your family or community. Remember to write your article to reflect what the verse says.

Providence to Progress

Write the correct answer.

> Bible   Darwin   injustices   pastors   providence
> research   scientists   seminary   social scientists   wisdom

_____ 1. belief that God rules over all; nothing happens apart from God's plan or permission

_____ 2. some of America's most respected leaders because they taught the Bible

_____ 3. school that trains pastors

_____ 4. what earlier generations read to find the solutions to their problems

_____ 5. people who replaced pastors for many Americans

_____ 6. man who taught that the world progressed the way it did because of nature and that God was not involved

_____ 7. authorities on American life who study societies

_____ 8. the surveys and experiments social scientists use to draw conclusions and solve problems

_____ 9. what science failed to give Progressives in their attempt to solve problems

_____ 10. what was created by forcing people to live by the Progressives' scientific ideas

Locate Proverbs 2:6 in the Bible. Write the verse and circle the word that tells who gives wisdom.

_____

_____

_____

HERITAGE STUDIES

Progressivism and Society

Complete the chart.

Changes Progressives wanted	Benefits and problems changes brought
make the places where people lived _____ and less _____	made people healthier
wanted clean _____	made people _____
end _____	sometimes made a better life for the poor
forbid _____	lessened problems caused by alcohol
wanted police to learn skills such as _____	better ability to capture criminals
wanted more _____ to prevent children from getting into _____	did not solve the problem of _____
wanted to change the way _____ were treated	was _____ to help prisoners change; was _____ to think that prisons were not for punishment; needed to fit the _____ with the crime
sought to change the way _____ were treated at _____	many state laws passed about _____ who worked; laws requiring children to attend _____
wanted employers to buy _____ insurance	possible to pay hurt workers
wanted to _____ education	high school students trained to go to _____; immigrant children sent to _____

Write the answers.

_____ 1. Having more of this by 1900 allowed Americans to enjoy sports, concerts, and other activities.

_____ 2. Many of their goals to solve problems were good, but some of their ideas did not really work.

_____ 3. the belief that nothing happens apart from God's plan or permission

_____ 4. These people became much wealthier than anyone else in the country.

_____ 5. Progressives wanted employers to buy this so they would have the money to pay hurt workers.

_____ 6. This group of people replaced pastors for many Americans when belief in providence began to change.

_____ 7. It is good to help these people change and become better people, but their punishment should fit the crime.

_____ 8. Progressives thought these people should run the schools instead of parents and communities.

_____ 9. They were concerned about their changing role in America as prices for food kept going down.

Progressivism & Government

Theodore Roosevelt

William Howard Taft

Woodrow Wilson

**Write *True* if the statement is true.
If the statement is false, write the correction for the underlined word.**

_____ 1. American Progressivism began in the <u>country</u>.

_____ 2. <u>Progressives</u> wanted their ideas to be law in the entire nation.

_____ 3. When people vote to choose who runs for office for each party, it is called a <u>direct primary</u>.

_____ 4. The Constitution gave state legislatures the power to select US <u>governors</u>.

_____ 5. The Founding Fathers wanted the <u>experts</u> to have a voice in the national government.

_____ 6. Progressives wanted to see <u>pastors</u> do more in government.

_____ 7. <u>Theodore Roosevelt</u> pushed many Progressive ideas.

_____ 8. <u>Woodrow Wilson</u> served under Roosevelt and followed him as president.

_____ 9. The <u>voters</u> thought the government should own the factories for all people.

HERITAGE STUDIES

Mark all the correct answers.

1. In what ways did Progressives and immigrants work together?
   ○ helped to make workers safer
   ○ promoted the culture of immigrants
   ○ worked to make city life better

2. Why did Progressives think immigrants were a problem?
   ○ thought immigrants did not celebrate their own culture in America
   ○ thought immigrants could change culture in America
   ○ thought immigrants brought crime and other evils with them

3. What did Progressives think about immigration changing culture?
   ○ Immigrants would not change the culture.
   ○ Immigrants might harm American culture.
   ○ Immigrants' cultures have good things that Americans can learn from.

4. What resulted from scientists arranging people into races?
   ○ caused everyone to be treated the same
   ○ caused belief that some races were superior to others
   ○ caused some people to be treated unjustly

5. How did black Americans deal with segregation?
   ○ Black Americans did not think they could end segregation.
   ○ Booker T. Washington wanted to bring about the end of segregation gradually.
   ○ Black Americans disagreed about how to deal with segregation.

6. What was Booker T. Washington known for?
   ○ led the Tuskegee Institute
   ○ was a freed slave who worked hard to gain an education
   ○ did not believe black Americans needed an education

7. What was W. E. B. Du Bois known for?
   ○ first black American to earn a PhD
   ○ was unconcerned about ending segregation
   ○ founded the National Association for the Advancement of Colored People (NAACP)

Automobiles and Airplanes

Refer to the Student Text to write the missing words to complete this section.

1. The first automobiles were very _____. Sometimes steam engines _____, and _____ cars could not be driven long distances.

2. Henry Ford's automobile ran on _____, used _____ parts, and was built on an _____ line.

3. People who bought automobiles could live in a _____ and work in a _____. People from the country could _____ into the city more often.

4. Ford showed businesses he could make more _____ by selling more automobiles to more people for _____ money. He also showed that by _____ his workers well, they could _____ to buy the products they were making.

Number the events in order.

_____ 5. The military began making planes that could be used in fighting.

_____ 6. The Wright brothers made the first successful flight.

_____ 7. The US Post Office began using airplanes to transport mail.

_____ 8. People used hot air balloons and gliders.

_____ 9. People looked for ways to use the airplane.

Art, Literature & Religion

Write the answers to each question.

1. Why did workers complain about working on the assembly line? _____

_____

_____

2. What was the financial situation of many people during the Progressive Era? _____

_____

_____

3. What was Edward Stratemeyer known for? _____

_____

_____

4. What bothered Americans about new styles of art produced at this time?

_____

_____

_____

Write the letter of the correct answer.

_____ 5. where science was taught and Christian ideas were dismissed as old-fashioned

_____ 6. what Christians were concerned might become unpopular

_____ 7. were willing to change Christianity

_____ 8. what was created when parts of Christianity were removed

_____ 9. traveled the country pointing out many problems in America

_____ 10. what evangelists said was a major danger to the Christian faith

_____ 11. what evangelists said was drawing many people away from God

_____ 12. where many Christians were strengthened and unbelievers often trusted Christ

> A. Christianity
> B. colleges
> C. enjoyments and comforts
> D. evangelists
> E. evangelists' meetings
> F. evolution
> G. false religion
> H. liberal Christians

Mark all the correct answers.

1. What describes life in the United States between 1900 and 1917?
   ○ spirituality   ○ problems   ○ progress

2. What problems with big businesses concerned some Americans?
   ○ wealth and power   ○ productivity   ○ conflict between owners and workers

3. What concerns did Americans have about children raised in tenements?
   ○ might not practice the skills needed to get good jobs
   ○ might follow bad influences
   ○ might not have the character to do good work

4. What did muckrakers write about?
   ○ good things   ○ villains   ○ bad news and sin

5. What did Populists want to see happen?
   ○ more government control
   ○ businesses to be bigger and more powerful
   ○ more power returned to the ordinary people

6. Who were some of the most respected leaders in the United States in the 1800s?
   ○ scientists   ○ pastors   ○ farmers

7. What describes God's providence?
   ○ happening according to God's plan or permission
   ○ God's rule over all
   ○ God's lack of involvement in the lives of men

Write the correct answers.

_____ 8. taught that the world progressed the way it did because of nature

_____ 9. replaced pastors for many Americans

_____ 10. studies societies

_____ 11. thought the country had problems and needed to make progress

_____ 12. what science failed to give Progressives

_____ 13. created by Progressives when they did not treat other people as being made in God's image

Write *True* if the statement is true.
If the statement is false, write the correction for the underlined word.

_____ 14. City playgrounds did not solve the problem of <u>education</u> as Progressives hoped they would.

_____ 15. Many Progressives did not look in the <u>newspaper</u> for wisdom.

_____ 16. Many states passed laws about <u>children</u> who worked.

_____ 17. Progressives wanted <u>colleges</u> to pay hurt workers.

_____ 18. Progressives thought <u>parents</u> needed to run the schools.

_____ 19. Progressivism began in the American <u>farms</u>.

_____ 20. Progressives changed how <u>senators</u> were elected.

Complete each statement.

21. _____ pushed Progressive ideas and was president from 1901 to 1909.

22. _____ followed Roosevelt as president.

23. _____ is the customs, beliefs, arts, and institutions of a group of people.

24. The law that said white and black Americans must stay separated was called

_____.

25. _____ followed Taft as president.

26. Booker T. Washington and _____ had different opinions on how to deal with segregation.

27. Henry Ford built an automobile that ran on _____.

28. Wilbur and Orville _____ built an airplane that could fly on its own power and was directed by a pilot.

29. College teachers turned to _____ as a source of truth.

30. _____ warned that many people were being drawn away from God.

Watching the War

Write _T_ if the statement is true. If the statement is false, draw a line through the incorrect part and write the correction in the blank.

_____ 1. President Wilson believed Americans should take sides in war.

_____ 2. Most Americans felt loyal to the Central Powers.

_____ 3. Germany placed ads in American newspapers warning the people not to travel on British ships.

_____ 4. Germany sank the _Lusitania_, a British warship.

_____ 5. To keep peace with the United States, Germany agreed to stop attacking ships that were not warships.

Complete the section.

6. Explain why many Americans felt loyal to the Allies. _____

_____

_____

_____

7. Explain why many Americans did not feel loyal to the Central Powers. _____

_____

_____

8. Explain Germany's unrestricted submarine warfare. _____

_____

_____

9. Would you have voted for Woodrow Wilson in 1916? Explain your answer.

_____

_____

Design a political propaganda poster to gain support for a candidate in the next presidential election.

Meatless and Wheatless

Prepare a menu to support the war effort.

	Meatless	Wheatless	Sweetless	Heatless
Breakfast	☐ Ceral ☐ eggs ☐ Yogort	☐ eggs ☐ bacon ☐ Jello	☐ Bread & B ☐ fruits	☐ fruits ☐ Ceral ☐ yogort
Lunch	☐ Salad ☐ Spagetti	☐ Salad ☐ Soup	☐ Salad ☐ Soup	☐ Salad ☐
Supper				

THIS STORE IS PLEDGED TO CONFORM TO THE
SUGAR REGULATIONS OF THE U.S. FOOD ADMINISTRATION

Your Sugar Ration is 2 lbs. per month

SUGAR 2 lbs.

SUGAR 1 lb. 1 oz.

SUGAR 11 oz.

AMERICA'S VOLUNTARY RATION
ENGLAND'S COMPULSORY RATION

FRANCE'S COMPULSORY RATION

ITALY'S COMPULSORY RATION

We must confine our consumption of Sugar
to not more than 2 lbs. per person per month
in order to provide a restricted ration
to England, France and Italy.

People often write poems to express something in a new way. The poems written during World War I help us understand how people felt about the war.

In a famous poem called "In Flanders Fields," Lieutenant Colonel John McCrae expressed his feelings about the soldiers who died.

In Flanders fields the poppies blow
Between the crosses, row on row,
That mark our place. . . .
. . . .
Short days ago
We lived, felt dawn, saw sunset glow,
Loved and were loved, and now we lie
In Flanders fields.

Write a poem about World War I.

_____

_____

_____

_____

_____

_____

_____

_____

American Allies

Answer the questions.

1. Who commanded the first American soldiers who arrived in France? _____

2. What were the American soldiers nicknamed? _____

3. What country withdrew from the war and left the Allies in desperate need of help? _____

4. What capital did the Americans play a key role in saving? _____

5. What did the French and Americans use to crush the German forces at Saint-Mihiel?

_____

6. What surprising killer spread among soldiers and other people around the world? _____

7. What country's fighter plane was used in World War I? _____

8. What were fighter pilots who shot down enemy planes called? _____

9. Who was the American ace who won twenty-six victories over other planes?

_____

10. What was Alvin York awarded? _____

11. What is an armistice? _____

12. What holiday is celebrated on November 11? _____

Write a paragraph describing how your family, church, or community celebrates Veterans Day.

Instructional Center for the 102d
Aero Squadron in France in 1917

_____

_____

_____

_____

_____

_____

_____

Mark the correct answer.

1. Which was not a reaction of the Allied nations when the war was over?
   - ○ singing, shouting, and dancing
   - ○ making a peace treaty in one day
   - ○ laughing and weeping at the same time
   - ○ ringing church bells

2. Which was not related to President Wilson's meeting with Allied leaders in France?
   - ○ a peace treaty
   - ○ fourteen points
   - ○ League of Nations
   - ○ land boundaries

3. Which was not related to Germany's part in the Treaty of Versailles?
   - ○ kept overseas landholdings
   - ○ paid France and Great Britain for their war costs
   - ○ lost land in Europe
   - ○ was blamed for the war

4. Which was not related to America's part in the treaty?
   - ○ America did not join the League of Nations.
   - ○ America worked out its own treaty with Germany.
   - ○ America joined the League of Nations and signed the Treaty of Versailles.
   - ○ America did not sign the Treaty of Versailles.

Write what you think a treaty to prevent more wars should contain.

_____

_____

_____

_____

_____

Henry Ford changed America's transportation. He perfected the mass production of the automobile. He manufactured a car called the Model T and made cars affordable for more people. Ford increased efficiency and speed in auto manufacturing by using an assembly line. Workers on an assembly line stand by a conveyor belt. Each worker adds a certain part to the product as quickly as possible.

Ford also standardized the parts so that cars could be repaired at a lower cost. Many manufacturers began to use an assembly line like the one developed by Ford. Products became more available and less expensive for everyone. The Fords had their home built in 1915 where they reared their son, Edsel Bryant Ford. Henry Ford's home became a National Historic Landmark in 1966 to honor his achievements.

Henry and Clara Ford's home was known as Fair Lane.

The moving assembly line was first used at the Ford Motor Company.

Write about a historic site you have visited or would like to visit.

_____

_____

_____

_____

_____

_____

_____

_____

Back to Normal

Match the description with the person or term.

_____ 1. president who said that America should focus mainly on business

_____ 2. place in New York City where the most important stock exchange is located

_____ 3. president who said he wanted a "return to normalcy"

_____ 4. person who owns stock in a company; a shareholder

_____ 5. person who is not serving in the military

_____ 6. money that banks give to their depositors

A. civilian
B. Calvin Coolidge
C. Warren G. Harding
D. interest
E. stockholder
F. Wall Street

Answer the questions in complete sentences.

7. What did Americans want now that the fighting was over?

_____

_____

_____

8. What did the factories focus on after World War I?

_____

_____

_____

9. Why did American businesses do well around the world after World War 1?

_____

_____

_____

Circle _S_ if the statement refers to the stock exchange or _B_ if the statement refers to a bank.

S   B   10. uses people's money to buy stocks

S   B   11. buys and sells stock

S   B   12. gives interest to depositors

Then and Now

Describe how the work was done before the invention and how the work is done today.

washing machine _____

_____

vacuum _____

_____

toaster _____

_____

electric stove _____

_____

A washboard was used for hand-washing clothing.

Circle the man if the sentence refers to men in the 1920s.
Circle the woman if the sentence refers to women in the 1920s.

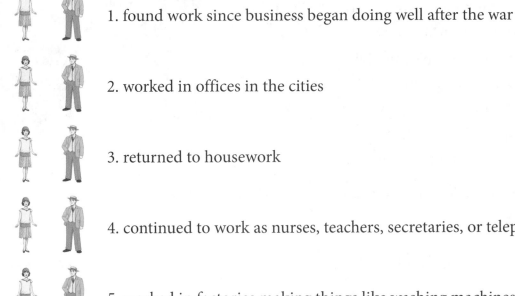

1. found work since business began doing well after the war

2. worked in offices in the cities

3. returned to housework

4. continued to work as nurses, teachers, secretaries, or telephone operators

5. worked in factories making things like washing machines, vacuums, and cars

List some of the things that were whirring, *vrooming*, and swishing in the "Roaring Twenties."

_____

_____

Match the person with the description.

_____ 1. Jack Dempsey

_____ 2. Gertrude Ederle

_____ 3. F. Scott Fitzgerald

_____ 4. George Gershwin

_____ 5. Charles Lindbergh

_____ 6. Babe Ruth

A. composer who combined traditional classical music and modern jazz
B. boxer
C. first woman to swim the English Channel
D. baseball star
E. novelist who wrote _The Great Gatsby_
F. first person to fly solo across the Atlantic

Mark all the correct answers.

7. How did the radio help change American living?
   ○ allowed people to hear news almost as soon as it happened
   ○ became a source of information and entertainment
   ○ helped families plan outings
   ○ provided a way for Americans to enjoy music, stories, and sports from their own homes

8. How did cars help change American living?
   ○ Families could plan an outing and pack a picnic lunch.
   ○ People could know the headlines from the news.
   ○ People could stop by roadside diners to eat.
   ○ People could drive from one state to another.

Describe what life would be like without cars.

Charles Lindbergh flew the _Spirit of St. Louis_ from New York to Paris, France.

_____

_____

_____

_____

_____

_____

_____

Mark the correct answer.

1. What do banks give to their depositors?
   ○ stocks   ○ interest   ○ deposit slips

2. What word describes when people put their money in a bank for safekeeping?
   ○ deposit   ○ stock exchange   ○ interest

3. What is a person called who does not serve in the military?
   ○ stockholder   ○ banker   ○ civilian

4. What is a person called who owns stock in a company?
   ○ stockholder   ○ anarchist   ○ civilian

5. What is a person called who believes that there should be no government?
   ○ civilian   ○ immigrant   ○ anarchist

6. What is organized crime?
   ○ many criminals who rob only banks
   ○ many criminals who work together to break the law
   ○ police who work together to catch criminals

Write the answer that completes each sentence.

_____ 7. The most famous baseball star in the 1920s was ____.

_____ 8. The first person to fly solo across the Atlantic was ____.

_____ 9. The most important stock exchange was located in New York City on ____.

_____ 10. Many people called the years between 1920 and 1929 ____.

Write *True* if the statement is true.
If the statement is false, write the correction for the underlined word.

_____ 11. Inventions such as the <u>washing machine</u> changed Americans' lives.

_____ 12. During the war, <u>many</u> people immigrated to the United States.

_____ 13. Violence during the Boston Police Strike left some Americans distrustful of <u>banks</u> and cities.

_____ 14. Criminals in Chicago in the Twenties were led by <u>Al Capone</u>.

Amendments

Write *18th* if the statement applies to the 18th Amendment.
Write *19th* if the statement applies to the 19th Amendment.

_____ 1. This amendment became law in 1919.

_____ 2. This amendment passed in 1920, soon after the war.

_____ 3. This amendment promised all women the right to vote.

_____ 4. This amendment made making, transporting, or selling any alcoholic beverage illegal.

_____ 5. This amendment dealt with women's suffrage.

_____ 6. This law is sometimes called Prohibition.

Match the words with the correct description.

_____ 7. medicine made from a mold that stops bacteria from growing

_____ 8. a throat infection that killed many people every year

_____ 9. a treatment for diabetes

> A. diphtheria
> B. insulin
> C. penicillin

Write an amendment for a law you would like to see changed in the Constitution.

_____

_____

_____

_____

_____

The Bible vs. Evolution

_____

Match the description to the person.

_____ 1. tried to prove that the Bible was full of errors

_____ 2. wrote many books to defend the Christian faith

_____ 3. left baseball to become an evangelist

_____ 4. supported the government's case that teachers
        must not teach evolution in public schools

_____ 5. broke the law by teaching evolution in the public school

A. William Jennings Bryan
B. Clarence Darrow
C. J. Gresham Machen
D. John Scopes
E. Billy Sunday

Write _F_ if the statement applies to the Fundamentalist.
Write _M_ if the statement applies to the Modernist.

_____ 6. believed modern science showed evolution was true

_____ 7. believed the Bible is God's Word

_____ 8. believed miracles were impossible

_____ 9. believed that history showed the Bible made mistakes

_____ 10. believed the Bible is more trustworthy than modern science or history

Write why you believe the Bible is true.

_____

_____

_____

_____

_____

Mark all the correct answers.

1. Why did the stock market collapse?
   - ○ The stock prices began to fall quickly.
   - ○ The bankers could not bring stock prices up.
   - ○ The stock prices began to go up.
   - ○ People stopped buying as much.

2. What happened after Black Tuesday?
   - ○ People lost the money they thought was safe.
   - ○ People bought fewer things.
   - ○ Workers from factories lost their jobs.
   - ○ Not many people were affected by the collapse of the stock market.

OCTOBER 1929

SUN	MON	TUES	WED	THUR	FRI	SAT
		1	2	3	4	5
6	7	8	9	10	11	12
13	14	15	16	17	18	19
20	21	22	23	24	25	26
27	28	29	30	31		

Match the words with the correct description.

_____ 3. nickname for October 29, 1929, when the stock market crashed

_____ 4. hard time in America's history

_____ 5. Republican candidate in the election of 1928

_____ 6. term for rising stock prices

_____ 7. Democratic candidate in the election of 1928

A. Herbert Hoover
B. Al Smith
C. bull market
D. Black Tuesday
E. Great Depression

Answer the questions.

8. How did advertising encourage people to buy things?

_____

_____

_____

9. Why did the stock market collapse?

_____

_____

10. What was the biggest problem that many Americans were confused about in the 1920s?

_____

_____

Define each term.

1. bull market _____

2. deposit _____

3. diphtheria _____

4. fundamental _____

5. insulin_____

6. interest _____

7. penicillin _____

8. Prohibition _____

Complete the sentence.

_____ 9. People who own stock in a company are called ____.

_____ 10. People who believe that there should be no government are called ____.

_____ 11. People who are not serving in the military are called ____.

_____ 12. A preacher who travels from city to city is called an ____.

_____ 13. Many criminals working together to break the law is called ____.

_____ 14. The most important stock exchange in New York City was located on ____.

Match the words with the correct phrase.

_____ 15. Clarence Birdseye

_____ 16. Clarence Darrow

_____ 17. Albert Einstein

_____ 18. Herbert Hoover

_____ 19. J. Gresham Machen

_____ 20. John Scopes

_____ 21. Billy Sunday

A. figured out how to freeze food well
B. was found guilty of teaching evolution
C. won the Nobel Prize for Physics
D. was the most respected Fundamentalist teacher
E. was sworn into office on March 4, 1929
F. defended John Scopes during the Scopes Trial
G. was the most famous of the Fundamentalist preachers

Write *True* if the statement is true.
If the statement is false, write the correction for the underlined words.

_____ 22. The <u>Boston Police Strike</u> caused looting and vandalization in Boston.

_____ 23. The washing machine and the <u>microwave</u> made housework easier in the Twenties.

_____ 24. Women often worked as <u>nurses</u> or secretaries in the Twenties.

_____ 25. Organized crime encouraged selling illegal alcohol and <u>looting</u>.

_____ 26. Two famous sports figures in the Twenties were Babe Ruth and <u>Jack Dempsey</u>.

Answer the questions.

27. Which amendment promised all women the right to vote? _____

28. Which amendment made it illegal to make, transport, or sell any alcoholic beverage?

_____

29. What word means "right to vote"? _____

30. What did Modernists believe? _____

_____

31. What happened on October 29, 1929, which was nicknamed Black Tuesday? _____

_____

32. What encouraged people to buy more things? _____

In 1792 a group of stockbrokers met under a buttonwood tree on Wall Street in New York City. They established rules for the buying and selling of shares in companies. They named their group the New York Stock Exchange (NYSE). Eventually the group moved to a building on Wall Street where it still operates today. It has become the world's largest stock exchange. It is sometimes just called Wall Street. In 1978 the building was designated a National Historic Landmark.

Signers of the Buttonwood Agreement

Stock certificate

Crash in America

Write the answer that completes each sentence.

_____ 1. The biggest stock market crash in American history happened in ____.

_____ 2. Some people would ____ on the stock market by buying stocks and then selling them as soon as the price went up.

_____ 3. The stock market crash was only one of many things that happened to bring about the ____.

_____ 4. To protect US businesses, Congress passed the Smoot-Hawley ____.

_____ 5. When many people rush the bank to withdraw money, the action is called a ____.

Write _True_ if the statement is true.
If the statement is false, write the correction for the underlined word.

_____ 6. The money to build more products to sell came from people who bought <u>stock</u> in companies.

_____ 7. Companies that sold stock often withheld <u>profits</u> from people who bought stocks.

_____ 8. The stock market crash showed that the US <u>banking system</u> was struggling.

_____ 9. People who borrow money from a bank must pay the loan back with <u>interest</u>.

_____ 10. The Bank of United States <u>was</u> owned by the United States government.

Complete the section.

11. Explain why Americans thought the economy would keep growing after Black Tuesday.

_____

_____

12. Explain how banks run out of money. _____

_____

_____

Making a Difference

Herbert Hoover headed efforts to provide food for people in Belgium during World War I. He ran the US Food Administration for troops. Hoover organized the relief effort when the Mississippi River flooded.

America has been blessed by God to be a land of plenty. But there are families across this nation who do not have enough food. There are many organizations that try to help. You can make a difference by organizing and distributing food for the needy.

1. Select and notify the group you will be collecting food for.

2. Determine the needs the group may have.

3. Determine how long the food drive will last.

4. Determine the amount of food to be collected.

5. Make collection containers.

6. Make posters. Include who will be receiving the food and what types of food are needed.

7. Deliver the food.

Write about the experience. Include your favorite part of the food drive.

_____

_____

_____

_____

_____

_____

_____

_____

_____

_____

Complete the section.

1. Explain how farmers could sell less produce but make more money. _____

_____

2. Explain how the Farm Bill hurt Americans. _____

_____

3. Explain how the Farm Bill hurt sharecroppers. _____

_____

4. Explain how Roosevelt stopped runs on the banks. _____

_____

5. Explain how the FDIC helped restore people's trust in banks. _____

_____

6. Explain how the law for businesses that sold stock made trading more just. _____

_____

Answer the questions using the graph on Student Text page 244.

7. What is the effect of overproduction? _____

8. What do lower prices lead to? _____

9. How would lower profits be hard on businesses? _____

_____

10. What do you think would be a good solution to help the economy grow? _____

_____

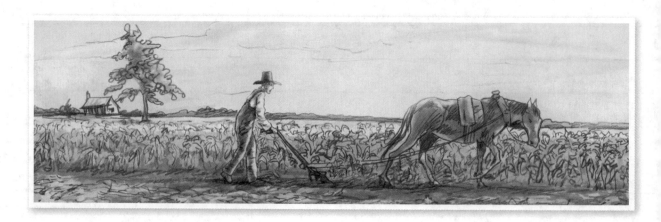

Mark all the correct answers.

1. What causes the stock market to crash?
   - ○ The economy is struggling.
   - ○ Stock market prices rise higher than what the companies are worth.
   - ○ Stocks gain more than half their value.

2. What contributed to the Great Depression?
   - ○ a growing economy
   - ○ the Smoot-Hawley Tariff Act
   - ○ runs on the banks

3. How did banks make money?
   - ○ receiving interest from loans
   - ○ placing a tariff on inventions
   - ○ investing in the stock market

4. Why did Americans think the economy would keep growing after Black Tuesday?
   - ○ Many new inventions were being sold.
   - ○ Companies were making money.
   - ○ Electricity became available.

Write _H_ if the statement applies to Hoover.
Write _R_ if the statement applies to Roosevelt.

_____ 5. promised the American people a New Deal

_____ 6. was an engineer and a problem solver

_____ 7. headed efforts to provide food for people in Belgium during World War I

_____ 8. was a great speaker on the radio

_____ 9. asked major business leaders not to cut people's wages

_____ 10. asked Congress to pass a bill that paid farmers to plant less

Write the answer that completes each sentence.

_____ 11. To buy stocks and then sell them as soon as the price goes up is to ____ on the stock market.

_____ 12. A tax against goods that are shipped into a country is called a ____.

_____ 13. To stop runs on the banks, Roosevelt declared a bank ____.

_____ 14. A person who checks business records is called an ____.

Write _True_ if the statement is true.
If the statement is false, write the correction for the underlined word.

_____ 15. The crash on Black Tuesday in 1929 was the <u>first</u> crash in American history.

_____ 16. The stock market crash showed that the US <u>economy</u> was struggling.

_____ 17. Hoover's plan to <u>lower</u> taxes hurt families and businesses and did not help to overcome the Great Depression.

_____ 18. The Farm Bill caused landowners to no longer need <u>sharecroppers</u> to work their land.

Overproduction drives prices down.

Lower prices lead to higher sales but lower profits.

Lower profits are hard on businesses and may lead to lower wages, fewer jobs, and going out of business.

Answer the questions about the graph.

19. Explain how overproduction hurts the economy. _____

_____

20. Explain how overproduction hurts businesses. _____

_____

Roosevelt's Programs

_____

Complete the web with your teacher.

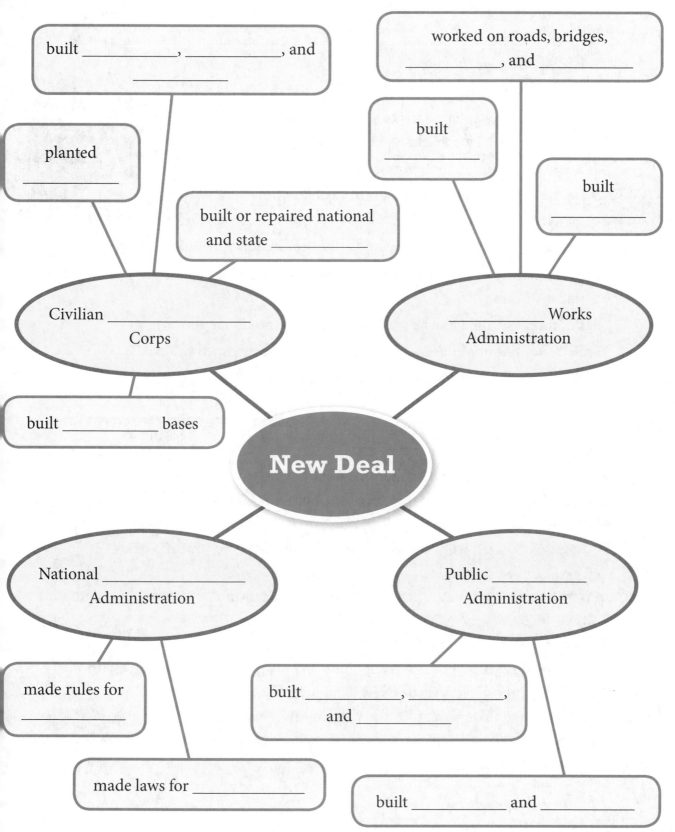

built _____, _____, and _____

planted _____

built or repaired national and state _____

Civilian _____ Corps

built _____ bases

worked on roads, bridges, _____, and _____

built _____

built _____

_____ Works Administration

New Deal

National _____ Administration

made rules for _____

made laws for _____

Public _____ Administration

built _____, _____, and _____

built _____ and _____

Match each cause with its effect. Choose the best answer.

Cause

_____ 1. Because of their money,

_____ 2. Because the replacement justices supported the New Deal,

_____ 3. Because they wanted to make sure that Roosevelt did not get any more New Deal laws passed,

_____ 4. Because he wanted their votes,

_____ 5. Because the government took responsibility for people's well-being,

_____ 6. Because it would help during and after the Great Depression,

_____ 7. Because the justices would support the New Deal and not declare it unconstitutional,

_____ 8. Because it seemed like he was trying to grab too much power,

_____ 9. Because the Supreme Court said that they were unconstitutional,

_____ 10. Because it would bring more voters to his party,

Effect

A. Roosevelt's Social Security Act became popular.

B. Roosevelt did not need to worry about the Supreme Court deciding it to be unconstitutional.

C. Roosevelt appointed work projects and gave out money to his supporters.

D. rich people lived secure lives.

E. conservative Democrats and conservative Republicans made sure none passed.

F. Roosevelt believed the New Deal should always exist.

G. Roosevelt worked to bring Republicans to his side.

H. nobody liked Roosevelt's plan to appoint more justices to the Supreme Court.

I. Roosevelt had to shut down the New Deal programs.

J. Roosevelt asked Congress to let him appoint more justices.

Define each term.

1. auditor _____

2. shanty _____

3. speculate _____

4. unemployment _____

Write *True* if the statement is true.
If the statement is false, write the correction for the underlined word.

_____ 5. A tax against goods that are shipped into a country is called a <u>tariff</u>.

_____ 6. To stop runs on the banks, Roosevelt declared a bank <u>audit</u>.

_____ 7. The stock market can crash when stock prices rise higher than the <u>companies</u> are worth.

_____ 8. Americans thought the economy would keep growing after Black Tuesday because many new <u>stocks</u> were being sold.

_____ 9. Roosevelt appointed work projects and gave out money to his supporters in exchange for their <u>votes</u>.

Write the answer that completes each sentence.

_____ 10. The crash on Black Tuesday in 1929 was the ____ crash in American history.

_____ 11. The stock market crash showed that the US ____ was struggling.

_____ 12. Hoover's plan to ____ taxes hurt families and businesses and did not help to overcome the Great Depression.

_____ 13. The Farm Bill caused the landowner to no longer need the ____ to work his land.

_____ 14. The stock market can crash when stocks quickly lose more than half their ____.

Mark all the correct answers.

15. Who promised the American people a New Deal?
    ○ Herbert Hoover
    ○ Franklin D. Roosevelt
    ○ Congress

16. Who asked major business leaders not to cut people's wages?
    ○ Herbert Hoover
    ○ Franklin D. Roosevelt
    ○ Congress

17. What did the Supreme Court say about many of the New Deal programs?
    ○ They were unconstitutional.
    ○ Roosevelt had to shut them down.
    ○ They were helping to end the Great Depression.

18. What is a city "machine"?
    ○ a group of businesses that run a city
    ○ a group of people who control how a city is run
    ○ a New Deal program

19. Who was to benefit from the Social Security Act?
    ○ older people
    ○ businesses
    ○ people who had lost their jobs

20. Who takes responsibility for people's well-being in a welfare state?
    ○ the worker
    ○ the government
    ○ the employer

21. Why did Roosevelt ask Congress to let him appoint more justices to the Supreme Court?
    ○ to keep the Supreme Court from declaring the New Deal unconstitutional
    ○ to keep businesses from failing
    ○ to allow him to have more justices who would support the New Deal

Write the event that happened on each date.

1. late 1943 _____

2. June 6, 1944 _____

3. May 8, 1945 _____

4. August 6, 1945 _____

Answer each question.

5. Why did it take a year for the Allies to free Europe? _____

_____

6. What plan did the Allies use so that they could easily bomb Tokyo and other important

cities? _____

7. Why wouldn't the Japanese surrender when the United States regularly dropped bombs on

their cities and ports and firebombed Tokyo? _____

_____

_____

8. What made the power of an atom bomb far greater than any other weapon in existence?

_____

Landing ships unloading cargo and an army convoy on Omaha Beach

Read the information with your teacher. Answer the questions.

Before the break of day on June 6, 1944, Allied paratroopers and soldiers in gliders began landing behind German lines in Normandy, France. At the same time, the largest amphibious invasion force in history moved across the English Channel toward the beaches of Normandy, twenty miles away. Allied air forces provided air protection. American soldiers landed on beaches code-named Utah and Omaha. The British landed on other nearby beaches code-named Juno, Gold, and Sword. This was "D-Day," the beginning of Operation Overlord. General Eisenhower announced by radio, "The tide has turned. The free men of the world are marching together to victory." This battle marked the beginning of the end of the war in Europe.

U.S. 6c POSTAGE

DWIGHT D. EISENHOWER

1. What did "D-Day" stand for? _____

2. Which Allied country was not involved in "D-Day"? _____

3. What country had defeated France? _____

4. Who provided air protection for the invasion forces? _____

5. What code names did America use for the beaches where its soldiers landed? _____

_____

6. What did the British name the beaches where they landed? _____

_____

7. What did General Eisenhower mean when he said, "The tide has turned"? _____

_____

_____

War in the Pacific

Refer to the Student Text pages 280–83. Mark your answers on the map.

1. Draw a box around the place where the Japanese attacked an American military base, resulting in the United States' declaring war on Japan.
2. Circle the island where an American victory was the turning point of the war in the Pacific. This tiny island lies about halfway between North America and Asia.
3. Draw a rectangle around the nation that attacked Pearl Harbor, Hawaii.
4. Draw a star by the nation that General Douglas MacArthur was in charge of defending.
5. Draw a triangle around the two places American forces captured that would make it easy to bomb Japan.
6. Draw diamonds around the cities where the first atomic bombs were dropped, leading to Japan's surrender.

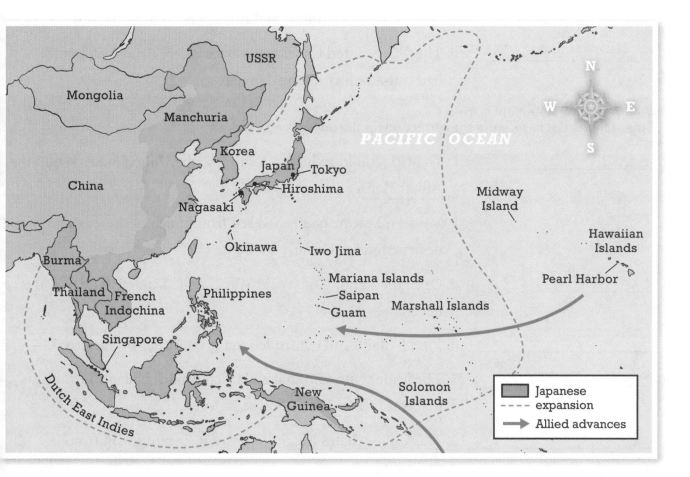

The World After the War

Write the word that completes each sentence.

_____ 1. The murder of Jews and other people is remembered as the ____.

_____ 2. Hitler killed about six ____ European Jews.

The state of Israel was established on May 14, 1948.

_____ 3. Corrie ten Boom and her family hid ____ in their house.

_____ 4. In 1948 the Jewish people set up their own state called ____.

_____ 5. After the war Germany and Japan needed to start new ____.

_____ 6. The ____ wanted to help countries where American bombs had caused much of the damage.

Write _True_ if the statement is true.
If the statement is false, write the correction for the underlined word.

_____ 7. To help rebuild industry in Europe, the United States set up the <u>Allied Plan</u>.

_____ 8. Western Europe had recovered from much of the war's physical destruction by the early <u>1970s</u>.

_____ 9. Once the fighting of World War II ended, a new type of <u>war</u> began.

_____ 10. Joseph Stalin still controlled many countries in Eastern <u>Asia</u>.

_____ 11. The leader who said that an "iron curtain" had cut Europe in half was <u>General Eisenhower</u>.

_____ 12. The United States fought to prevent <u>Communism</u> from spreading.

_____ 13. As Americans celebrated the victory against Germany and Japan, few thought about problems with <u>Russia</u>.

The Niagara Falls are situated in two different countries. There are three different waterfalls that make up Niagara Falls. Two of the falls are in New York State, and the other is mostly in Ontario, Canada. American Falls, Bridal Veil Falls, and Horseshoe Falls combined produce more than 3,000 tons of falling water every second. The force of this water is enough to generate over 4,000,000 kilowatts of electricity.

Established in 1885, Niagara Falls State Park is America's oldest state park. About 400 acres have been reserved in this state park. Niagara Falls State Park was designed by Frederick Law Olmsted. Visitors can do much more than watch the majestic waterfalls. They can take a boat ride on the *Maid of the Mist*, visit an aquarium, or hike one of the park's many trails. An observation tower offers a view of all three waterfalls.

Complete the puzzle.

Across

2. what visitors ride to see the waterfalls up close; *Maid of the Mist*
4. falls that are situated in two different countries
6. what offers a view of all three waterfalls
9. what the force of the water generates

Down

1. country where only one of the Niagara Falls is located
3. amount of land that has been reserved for the park is four hundred of these
5. country where two of the Niagara Falls are located
7. person who designed the state park (last name)
8. number of waterfalls that make up Niagara Falls

Answer the questions.

1. How many states make up the Northeast region? _____

2. Who helped the Pilgrims survive in America? _____

   _____

3. Which two states were home to the Lenape Indians? _____

4. What was the name of the largest Indian group in the Northeast? _____

5. Where were the first battles of the Revolutionary War fought? _____

6. Which of the Northeastern colonies was the first to become a state? _____

7. List two important American documents written in the Northeast. _____

   _____

8. List two national landmarks found in the Northeast. _____

Answer in complete sentences.

9. Explain what happened at the Boston Tea Party.

   _____

   _____

   _____

10. Describe the practices of the Puritans.

   _____

   _____

   _____

   _____

Write the names of the states in the Northeast region.

1. _____

2. _____

3. _____

4. _____

5. _____

6. _____

7. _____

8. _____

9. _____

10. _____

11. _____

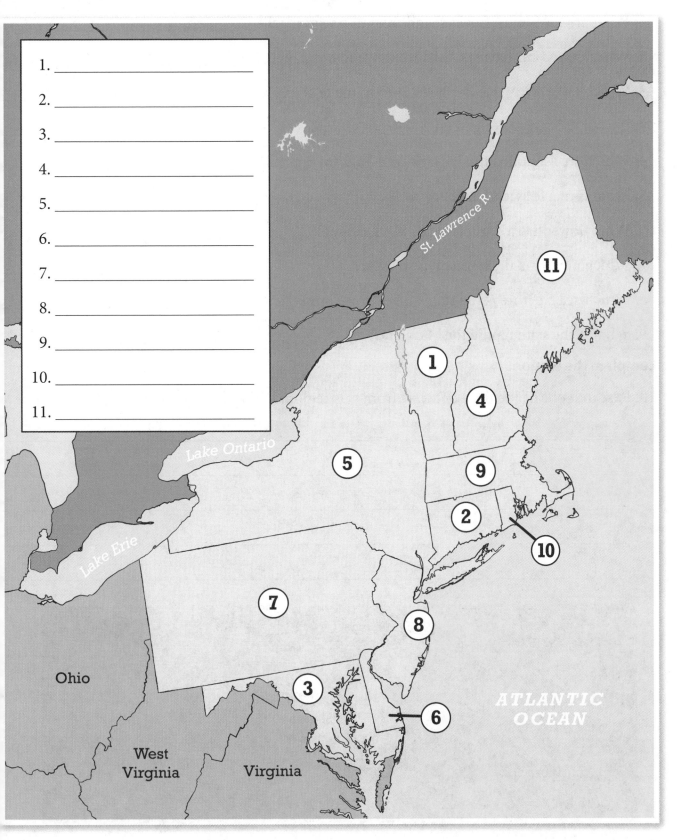

Flora and Fauna

_____

Answer the questions.

1. What are the plants, flowers, and trees in a region called? _____

2. What are the animals and birds that live in a region called? _____

3. Which tall, sturdy tree has been used to make ships' masts for hundreds of years? _____
   _____

4. Which tree supplied the Indians with bark for canoes? _____

5. What is maple syrup made from? _____

6. What flower has a dome-shaped black center? _____

7. Which animal is the largest type of deer? _____

8. Which sea creature is the state animal for Connecticut? _____

9. What is the state reptile for Maryland? _____

Complete the section.

10. Research one of the flora or fauna from this region. Write about your findings.

   _____

   _____

   _____

   _____

   _____

Natural Resources

_____

Write NE if the description applies to the New England states.
Write MA if the description applies to the Middle Atlantic states.

_____ 1. Colonists from England settled this area.

_____ 2. States that make up this area include
Maine, Vermont, New Hampshire,
Massachusetts, Connecticut, and Rhode
Island.

_____ 3. States that make up this area include
New York, Pennsylvania, New Jersey,
Maryland, and Delaware.

_____ 4. This area has mostly mild springs, humid summers, and cold winters.

_____ 5. This area has many natural seaports that provide lobster and many kinds of fish.

_____ 6. This area has fertile soil that provides grassy land for dairy farming.

Answer the questions.

7. How did the colonists from England find the climate in New England? _____

8. What do the forests of New England provide? _____

9. What affects the climate of Middle Atlantic states? _____

10. What grows well in New Jersey's humid climate? _____

11. Where in New Jersey is an ideal place to grow cranberries? _____

12. Where in Maryland do crabs and oysters live? _____

Refer to Student Text page 299 to list resources found in the Northeast region.

_____

_____

_____

_____

Industries

Mark all the correct answers.

1. Which of the following describes an industry?
   - ○ major ways people make a living
   - ○ goods or services produced
   - ○ work created from an area's natural resources

2. What industries do the maple trees in New England create?
   - ○ tourism
   - ○ coal
   - ○ syrup

3. What natural resource do New York and Pennsylvania have that provides a major industry?
   - ○ seaports
   - ○ trees
   - ○ coal
   - ○ fertile land

4. What do truck farms in New Jersey grow to sell?
   - ○ dairy products
   - ○ fruits
   - ○ animals
   - ○ vegetables

5. What manufacturing industry do some states in the Northeast region have?
   - ○ dairy
   - ○ chemical
   - ○ computer
   - ○ syrup

6. What service industries are most common in the Northeast?
   - ○ computer
   - ○ medicine
   - ○ insurance
   - ○ theater

7. What natural resources allow states in the Northeast region to be leaders in the fishing industry?
   - ○ Chesapeake Bay
   - ○ Pacific Ocean
   - ○ Atlantic Ocean

8. What state is the top producer of lobsters?
   - ○ Maryland
   - ○ New York
   - ○ Maine
   - ○ New Jersey

9. What is New York City's most important industry?
   - ○ dairy farming
   - ○ publishing
   - ○ fishing
   - ○ money

10. What industry in New York City is the largest business of its kind in the world?
    - ○ insurance
    - ○ fishing
    - ○ art
    - ○ New York Stock Exchange

Complete the section.

11. List the major industries in the Northeast region.

    _____

12. Describe the process of making maple syrup.

    _____

    _____

    _____

HERITAGE STUDIES

_____

Match the term with the definition.

_____ 1. continental

_____ 2. fauna

_____ 3. flora

_____ 4. industry

_____ 5. truck farms

_____ 6. wetland

A. plants, flowers, and trees in a region
B. small farms that grow fruits and vegetables to sell
C. animals and birds that live in a region
D. states located on a continent
E. bog or swamp area that is soaked with water
F. major way the people in a region make a living by the goods or services produced

Complete each sentence.

_____ 7. The Indian who helped the Pilgrims survive in America was ___.

_____ 8. The event in which citizens of Boston dumped British tea into the harbor became known as the ____.

_____ 9. Two important documents that were signed in Philadelphia
_____ were the ____ and the ____.

_____ 10. The statue standing in New York Harbor that symbolizes America's freedom and opportunity is the ____.

_____ 11. The religious group of European settlers that settled in the Northeast in the 1600s was the ____.

_____ 12. The six states in the upper Northeast are called the ____ states.

_____ 13. The five states in the lower Northeast are called the ____ states.

_____ 14. An important resource in New York's river valleys is their ____.

_____ 15. Industries are often created by an area's ____.

_____ 16. The states along the Atlantic coast are leaders in the ____ industry.

Write the names of the states.

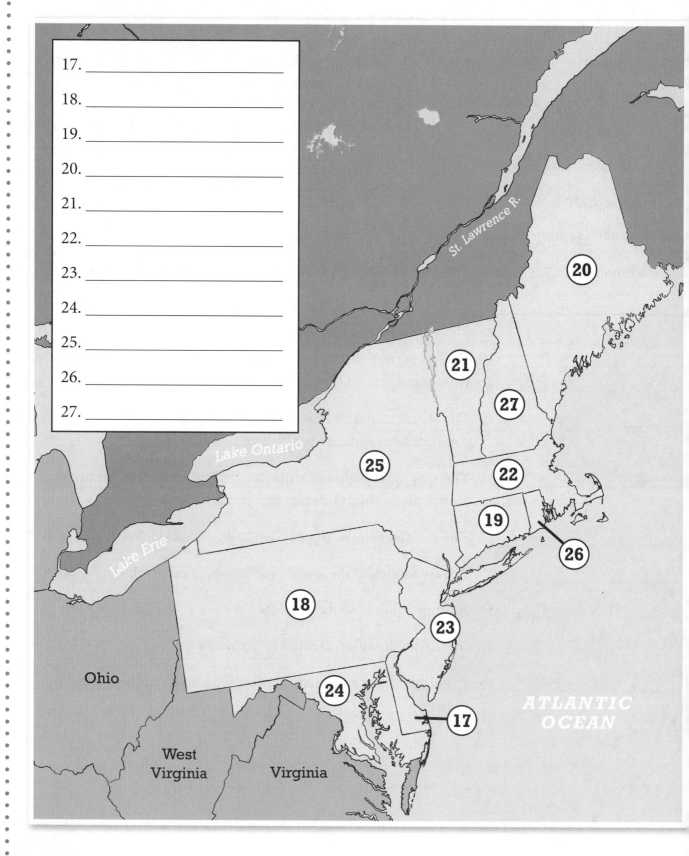

17. _____

18. _____

19. _____

20. _____

21. _____

22. _____

23. _____

24. _____

25. _____

26. _____

27. _____

Mark the city where each site can be found.

	New York City	Philadelphia	Boston	Baltimore
Fort McHenry				
replica of the Boston Tea Party ship				
Independence Hall				
the Bronx, Manhattan, Queens, Brooklyn, and Staten Island				
house of Betsy Ross				
mouth of the Hudson River				
Old South Meeting House				
Carpenters' Hall				
house of Paul Revere				

Complete each sentence.

_____   1. Many people living close together makes a city's population ____.

_____   2. New York City is made up of five counties called ____.

_____   3. The two important documents that were signed in
_____   Philadelphia were the ____ and the ____.

_____   4. Many people like to visit the Boston Harbor to see a replica of the ship from the ____.

_____   5. The poem written by Francis Scott Key that later became America's national anthem was ____.

Reading a Demographic Chart

Refer to the demographic charts to answer the questions.

A study of human populations is called **demography**.

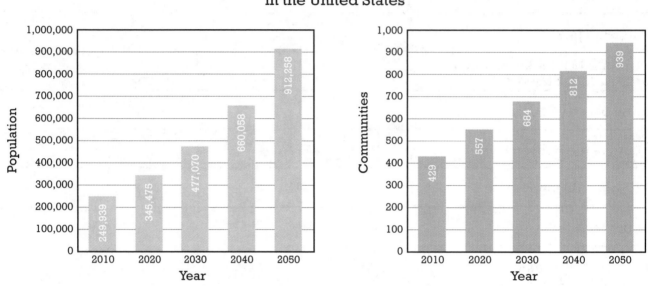

Growing Amish Population
in the United States

1. In what year is the Amish population expected to be the greatest? _____

2. How many Amish communities are expected to exist in the year 2050? _____

3. Between which two years is the greatest increase in the number of Amish communities expected? _____

4. What can you conclude about the growing Amish population when compared with the growth of Amish communities? _____

_____

_____

Define each term.

1. boroughs _____

2. continental _____

3. demographics _____

4. dense _____

5. fauna _____

6. flora _____

7. truck farm _____

8. wetland _____

Answer the questions.

_____ 9. What did some citizens of Boston dump into the harbor because they did not want to pay the British tax?

_____ 10. What group of people came to America to freely practice their faith?

_____ 11. In what city in Pennsylvania were the Declaration of Independence and the US Constitution signed?

_____ 12. What are the six states in the upper Northeast often called?

_____ 13. What are the five states in the lower Northeast called?

_____ 14. Through what major way do people in a region make a living?

_____ 15. What is the largest mountain range in the Northeast?

Complete the section.

16. Explain the ways regions are unique.

_____

17. List the major industries in the Northeast region.

_____

_____

Write the letter for each state.

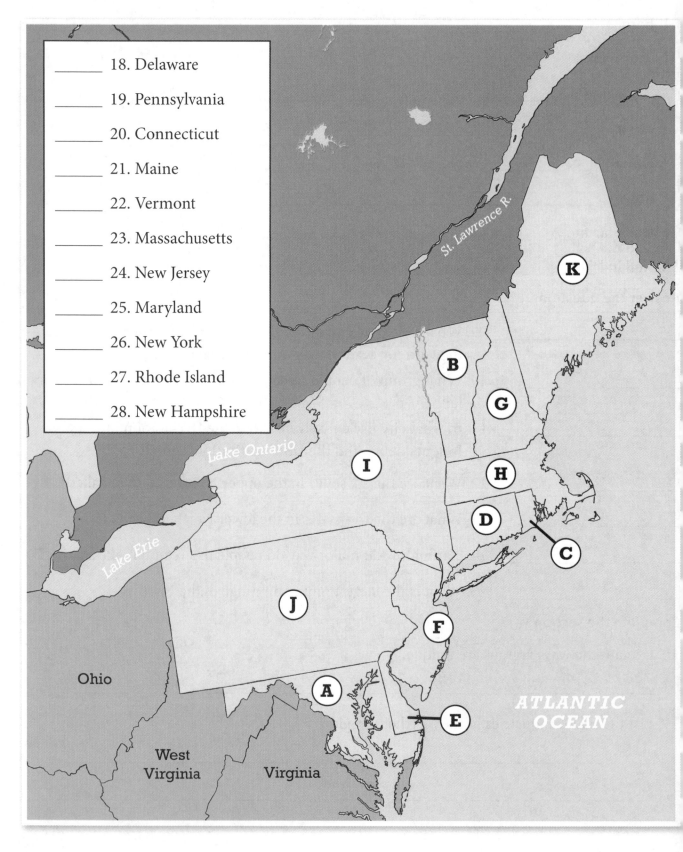

_____	18. Delaware
_____	19. Pennsylvania
_____	20. Connecticut
_____	21. Maine
_____	22. Vermont
_____	23. Massachusetts
_____	24. New Jersey
_____	25. Maryland
_____	26. New York
_____	27. Rhode Island
_____	28. New Hampshire

Read the article with your teacher.

Fort Sumter is located in the harbor of Charleston, South Carolina. The first shots of the Civil War were fired on the fort in 1861. Union soldiers manned the fort, knowing that they might go to war with the Confederacy. Citizens of Charleston were angry about being stuck in the middle. Both the North and the South recognized Charleston Harbor as an important shipping port. Both sides wanted to control the harbor. After the Union soldiers surrendered the fort, the Confederacy held it throughout the war.

The building of Fort Sumter was not fully completed before the Civil War began. After the war, the fort lay in ruins. It was rebuilt and manned again during World Wars I and II. Now it is a national monument. Visitors can tour the museum and the fort to learn about

its history. The fort also houses guns from the Civil War era. Five historic flags fly above the fort. These flags include two United States flags, two Confederate flags, and the South Carolina state flag. A current US flag stands in the middle.

Write a sentence to answer each question.

1. Why did both Union and Confederate soldiers want to control Charleston Harbor?

_____

2. Why did the Union soldiers man the fort?

_____

3. How did the Confederacy get control of the fort?

_____

4. What was the condition of Fort Sumter after the Civil War? _____

5. Why do you think the United States rebuilt and manned Fort Sumter during World Wars I and II? _____

6. Why might the United States (Union), Confederate, and South Carolina flags fly above the fort? _____

_____

A Unique Region

Match the term with the definition.

_____ 1. first English settlement in America

_____ 2. Indian tribe that built large mounds as part of its religion

_____ 3. the Cherokee, Creek, Choctaw, and Chickasaw tribes once lived in this region

_____ 4. thatched-roof homes without walls

_____ 5. the reason most Indians of the Southeast had to move west

_____ 6. Indian tribe that was known for its cypress canoes

_____ 7. leader of the Continental Army during the Revolutionary War

_____ 8. one reason the Southeast became one of the most religious parts of the United States

A. Indian Removal Act
B. Seminole
C. Jamestown
D. Southeast
E. George Washington
F. chickees
G. Great Awakening
H. Natchez

Write _True_ if the statement is true.
If the statement is false, write the correction for the underlined word.

_____ 9. Leaders in the South wanted people to have good <u>houses</u>.

_____ 10. Southern people believed a man should own his own <u>land</u> to support himself and his family.

_____ 11. <u>Hospitality</u> made it possible for Southern leaders to live the life of a gentleman, to own large plantations, and to pursue learning.

_____ 12. Southerners preferred <u>farming</u> over trade and manufacturing.

_____ 13. Many slaves accepted <u>Christianity</u>.

Southeast Region

Fill in the names of the states in the Southeast region.

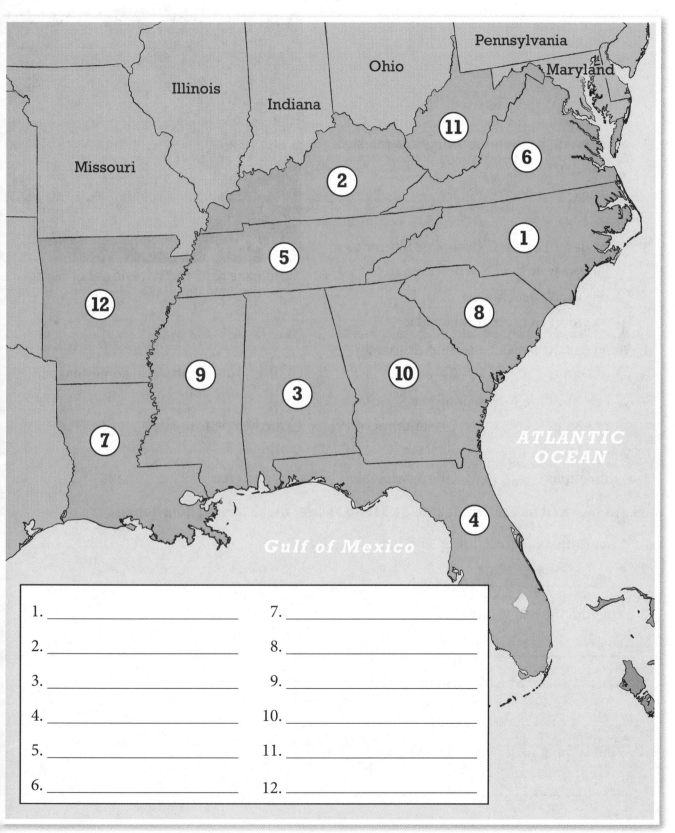

1. _____   7. _____

2. _____   8. _____

3. _____   9. _____

4. _____   10. _____

5. _____   11. _____

6. _____   12. _____

Flora and Fauna

Mark all the correct answers.

1. What is an example of an area of land covered by water?
   - ○ plain
   - ○ marsh
   - ○ swamp

2. What might be found growing in a marsh?
   - ○ sweet grass
   - ○ ferns
   - ○ orchids

Cherokee rose, the state flower of Georgia

3. What describes the Okefenokee Swamp?
   - ○ largest swamp in North America
   - ○ dry sandy beach
   - ○ found in Georgia and Florida

4. What usually lives in a swamp or marsh?
   - ○ alligators
   - ○ people
   - ○ fish, frogs, toads, and some snakes

5. Which birds are found along the Southeast coastline?
   - ○ cardinals
   - ○ sandpipers
   - ○ brown pelicans

6. What is West Virginia's state tree?
   - ○ magnolia
   - ○ sugar maple
   - ○ palm tree

Refer to the chart on Student Text page 318 to answer the following questions.

7. What is the state tree, flower, and bird of Georgia?

   _____

8. What does the state flower of Arkansas tell you about this state?

   _____

9. Which two state birds are state symbols of more than one state?

   _____

10. What is the state flower of Florida?

   _____

The Nature of the Place

Match the information with the correct term.

_____ 1. area made up of sandy beaches in some parts and marshes or swamps in other parts

_____ 2. flatland stretching up from the coast

_____ 3. flat or hilly land beyond the mountains

_____ 4. foothills between the coastal plain and the mountains

> A. coastal plain
> B. piedmont
> C. plateau
> D. coastland

Write _True_ if the statement is true.
If the statement is false, write the correction for the underlined word.

_____ 5. The Mississippi River is the longest river in the <u>world</u>.

_____ 6. The Southeastern states face dangers from <u>hurricanes</u>.

_____ 7. The Southeast climate tends to be <u>harsher</u> than other regions overall.

_____ 8. The warm weather in the Southeast allows plants to grow for <u>short</u> parts of the year.

_____ 9. The climate becomes <u>warmer</u> the farther north you go into the Southeastern mountains.

Write the correct word to complete the sentence.

_____ 10. Several states have built important _____ because of the long coastline with natural harbors.

_____ 11. Goods can be shipped up and down some of the _____ in the Southeast.

_____ 12. Coal, oil, and natural gas are resources that provide _____ for many Americans.

_____ 13. Pottery can be made from _____ found in the Southeast.

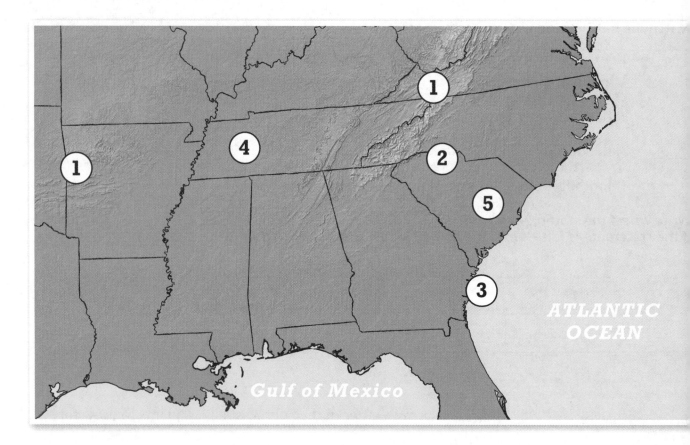

Write the term for the type of landform that matches each number on the map.
Use Student Text page 319.

1. _____

2. _____

3. _____

4. _____

5. _____

coast
coastal plains
mountains
piedmont
plains

Write the name of two mountain ranges in the Southeast region.

6. _____

7. _____

_____

Mark all the correct answers.

1. Who were some of the people who lived in the Southeast in the earliest days?
   - ○ European colonists
   - ○ Natchez
   - ○ Seminoles

2. Which things describe the Indian peoples in the Florida area?
   - ○ built large mounds as part of their religion
   - ○ lived in thatched-roof homes called chickees
   - ○ used cypress canoes

3. What is true of the first English settlement in America?
   - ○ was called Jamestown
   - ○ disappeared mysteriously
   - ○ was found in the Southeast

4. Which war's important battles were fought in the first colonies of the United States?
   - ○ the Spanish-American War
   - ○ the Civil War
   - ○ the Revolutionary War

5. What is true about religion in the Southeast?
   - ○ The Great Awakening changed religion in the South and Southeast.
   - ○ Few people practice religion in the Southeast.
   - ○ The Southeast is one of the most religious regions in the United States.

6. Which things characterized Southern life?
   - ○ preference of farming over trade and manufacturing
   - ○ hospitality
   - ○ politeness and good manners

Match the description to the correct term.

_____ 7. sad part of Southern culture that made it possible for Southern leaders to live the life of a gentleman, to own large plantations, and to pursue learning

_____ 8. a separation between black and white Americans

_____ 9. black Americans' struggle to gain equality

> A. segregation
> B. slavery
> C. civil rights movement

Write the correct answer for each definition.

_____ 10. area covered by shallow water in which small plants grow

_____ 11. area covered by water in which larger plants and trees grow

_____ 12. largest swamp in North America

_____ 13. bird with a pouch under its long bill

_____ 14. ground that rises as you move westward away from the Atlantic Ocean

_____ 15. flatland stretching up from the coast

_____ 16. main mountains found in the Southeast

_____ 17. flat or hilly land beyond the mountains

_____ 18. longest river in the United States

_____ 19. a danger in the Southeast due to location and climate

_____ 20. elements of Southeast climate that cause plants to grow well

_____

_____ 21. busy place where goods can be shipped to and received from countries all over the world

_____ 22. a barrier built on rivers to help control flooding and to generate power

_____ 23. resource used for gravel and cement

_____ 24. provision produced from coal, oil, or natural gas

Making a Living

Complete the chart.

Southeastern Economy	
what ports are used for	
states that grow both tobacco and cotton	
types of produce grown	
animals farmers raise	
natural fuel resources	
cloth manufacturing	
food that is processed	
items made from metal or plastic	
attractions for tourists	
businesses using human resources	

Write about the industry in the Southeast you would want to work in and tell why.

_____

_____

_____

_____

Cities in the Southeast

Write *WDC* if the photo applies to Washington, DC.
Write *RV* if the photo applies to Richmond, Virginia.
Write *CNC* if the photo applies to Charlotte, NC.
Write *CSC* if the photo applies to Charleston, SC.

_____ 1.

A large banking center

_____ 2.

Confederate capitol

_____ 3.

Fort Sumter

_____ 4.

White House

Write *SG* if the photo applies to Savannah, Georgia.
Write *AG* if the photo applies to Atlanta, Georgia.
Write *NOL* if the photo applies to New Orleans, Louisiana.
Write *MT* if the photo applies to Memphis, Tennessee.

_____ 5.

Martin Luther King Jr.

_____ 6.

Creole food

_____ 7.

Park in a ward

_____ 8.

Center for movement of goods

States of the Southeast Region

Write the name of the state that matches the number on the map.

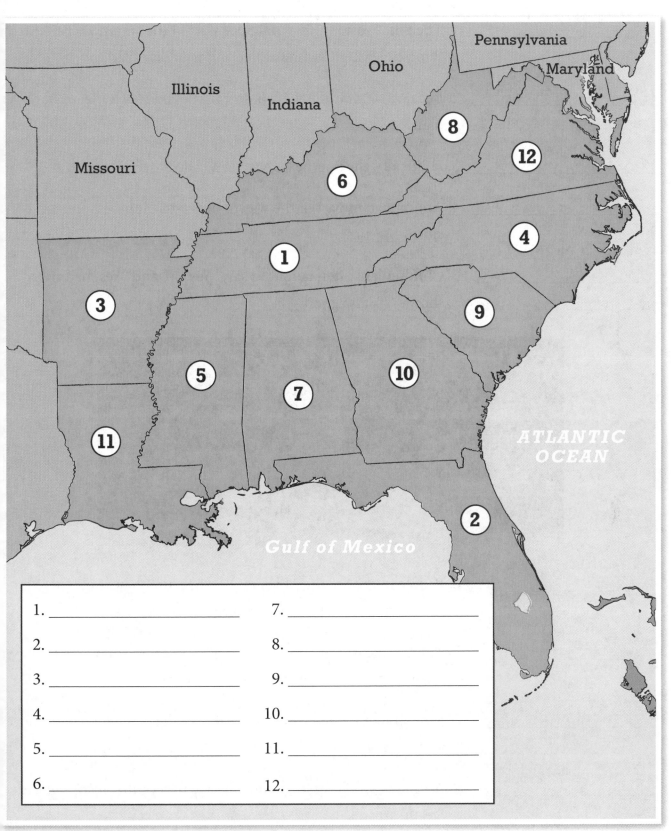

1. _____	7. _____
2. _____	8. _____
3. _____	9. _____
4. _____	10. _____
5. _____	11. _____
6. _____	12. _____

People of the Southeast

_____

Write the correct word to complete the sentence.

_____ 1. The Southeast is a very religious part of the country where many Bible-believing Christians live and is often called the ____.

_____ 2. Because of their religious past, Miami and New Orleans have many ____.

_____ 3. Politically, the Southeast has been called the ____.

_____ 4. An important part of the way of life in the Southeast region is close ____ ties.

_____ 5. Children are often taught to say, "Yes sir" and "Yes ma'am" to
_____ show ____ and good ____.

_____ 6. People in the Southeast value ____ because they know there is much wisdom in the way people lived in the past.

_____ 7. The Southeast region has a long ____ because some of its states were the first to enter the United States.

_____ 8. Sad parts of the Southeast's history are the ____, segregation, and slavery.

_____ 9. A time of God's blessing and a happy part of the history of the Southeast was the ____.

Match the term with the correct definition.

_____ 1. changed spiritual life in the South and Southeast

_____ 2. ended slavery and freed black Americans

_____ 3. built large mounds as part of their religion

_____ 4. became the first president of the United States and was from the Southeast

_____ 5. made cypress canoes and built thatched-roof homes called chickees

_____ 6. songs by slaves that often had ideas from Scripture

_____ 7. is the largest swamp in North America

_____ 8. is an area covered by shallow water in which small plants grow

_____ 9. is an area covered by water where larger plants and trees grow

A. spirituals
B. marsh
C. Natchez
D. Okefenokee Swamp
E. Seminoles
F. George Washington
G. swamp
H. Great Awakening
I. Civil War

Write the correct word to complete the sentence.

_____ 10. Land made up of sandy beaches in some places and marshes or swamps in other parts is called the ____.

_____ 11. Flat or hilly land beyond the mountains is called a ____.

_____ 12. Ground that rises as you move westward away from the Atlantic Ocean is called the ____.

_____ 13. Flatland stretching up from the coast is called the ____.

Mark all the correct answers.

14. Which of the following show the importance of the ocean to business in the Southeast?
    ○ ports for shipping goods
    ○ mountain hiking
    ○ fishing industry
    ○ tourism

15. What do farmers produce in the Southeast?
    ○ citrus fruits and sugarcane
    ○ apples, soybeans, and peanuts
    ○ dairy and beef cattle
    ○ automobiles

16. What are some natural resources in the Southeast for producing energy?
    ○ coal   ○ natural gas   ○ electricity   ○ oil

17. What contributes to the economy of the Southeast?
    ○ manufacturing   ○ banking   ○ tourism   ○ agriculture

Write the name of the state that matches the number on the map.

18. _____

19. _____

20. _____

21. _____

22. _____

23. _____

24. _____

25. _____

26. _____

27. _____

28. _____

29. _____

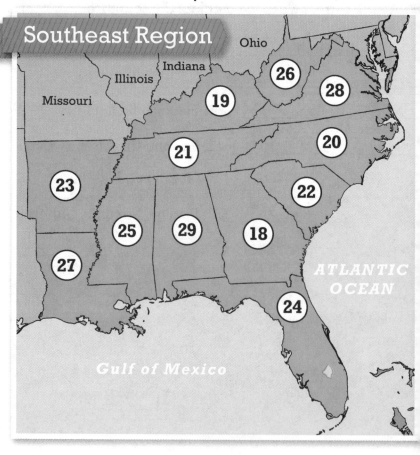

Mount Rushmore is a national memorial located in the Black Hills National Forest near Keystone, South Dakota. The memorial shows the faces of four United States presidents sculpted into the side of the mountain. The four presidents are George Washington, Thomas Jefferson, Theodore Roosevelt, and Abraham Lincoln. Many have called Mount Rushmore the "Shrine of Democracy."

The sculpture was designed by Gutzon Borglum, and he directed the construction process. The sculpture took fourteen years to build. Nearly 400 people worked on it from 1927 to 1941. Borglum died months before the sculpture was completed.

Today visitors to Mount Rushmore can see the sculpture from a large platform, or they can walk along the Presidential Trail for a closer view.

Choose one of the four presidents honored on Mount Rushmore and write two paragraphs about his life. Include his accomplishments, the dates he was president, and why you think he was chosen to be part of this memorial.

_____

_____

_____

_____

_____

_____

_____

_____

_____

_____

_____

_____

Shaped by Its Past

Fill in the blanks and then number the events in the order they occurred.

_____ 1. Americans poured into the Midwest during the _____.

_____ 2. During the 1900s _____ worked with farmers to produce

hardier _____ and better _____.

_____ 3. The _____, _____, and

_____ Indians lived across the region.

_____ 4. _____ from northern Europe often ended up in the

_____ Midwestern states.

_____ 5. During the 1700s _____ settlers trickled into the area.

Use the Glossary to define each term.

6. prairie _____

_____

7. tributary _____

_____

8. aquifer _____

_____

Write the name of the Midwestern author who helped shape America.

_____ 9. wrote about life in the Nebraska prairies

_____ 10. told stories about the 1920s

_____ 11. wrote about growing up in several Midwestern states

What helped produce the Midwestern culture?

_____

_____

_____

Bright and Beautiful

Read the article.

The pasqueflower became the state flower of South Dakota in 1903. The flower's name refers to Easter. Near the Easter season the pasqueflower peeks through the snow to welcome spring. It grows close to the ground and bears lovely lavender, blue, or white flowers with yellow stamens in the center. Silky hairs cover the green leaves and stem, and all three help protect the plant against the cold. This flower grows in dry soil with gravel and sand. It grows on the south side of slopes and grows well in tundras. The pasqueflower is one of the beautiful flowers that grows in the Midwest.

Answer the questions.

1. Which state made the pasqueflower its state flower in 1903? _____

_____

2. What time of year does the pasqueflower appear? _____

_____

3. What do the silky hairs, green leaves, and stem do for the plant? _____

_____

4. Why would this plant not be found growing in a marsh or swamp? _____

_____

5. Color the flower on the page as described in the article. _____

_____

Match the definition with the correct term.

_____ 1. There is an unfinished carving of this Sioux war chief in Thunderhead Mountain.

_____ 2. When this was found, the Sioux were forced off the land in the Black Hills.

_____ 3. These famous highlands rise in southern Missouri and neighboring states.

_____ 4. Kansas and Nebraska lie in this area known for severe thunderstorms.

_____ 5. These rooms dug into the ground give refuge to people when a severe thunderstorm comes.

_____ 6. This name was given to a highland region of South Dakota because of the trees covering the slopes of the hills.

_____ 7. This memorial has the faces of four presidents carved into its rock.

A. Black Hills
B. Crazy Horse
C. gold
D. Mount Rushmore
E. Ozark Mountains
F. storm cellars
G. Tornado Alley

Complete the sentence.

8. Minnesota's legendary hero famous for logging in the state's woods is _____.

9. Good soil that farmers can use to raise crops is called _____ land.

10. People enjoy fishing and sightseeing on the _____ running through the Midwest.

11. The Minnesota Mesabi Range is rich with _____.

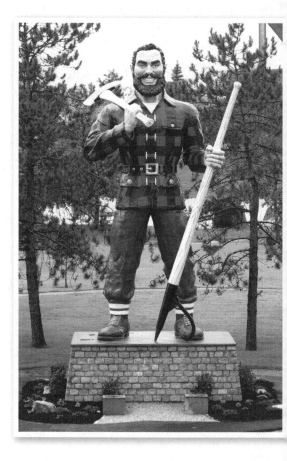

Write the name of the state that matches each number on the map.

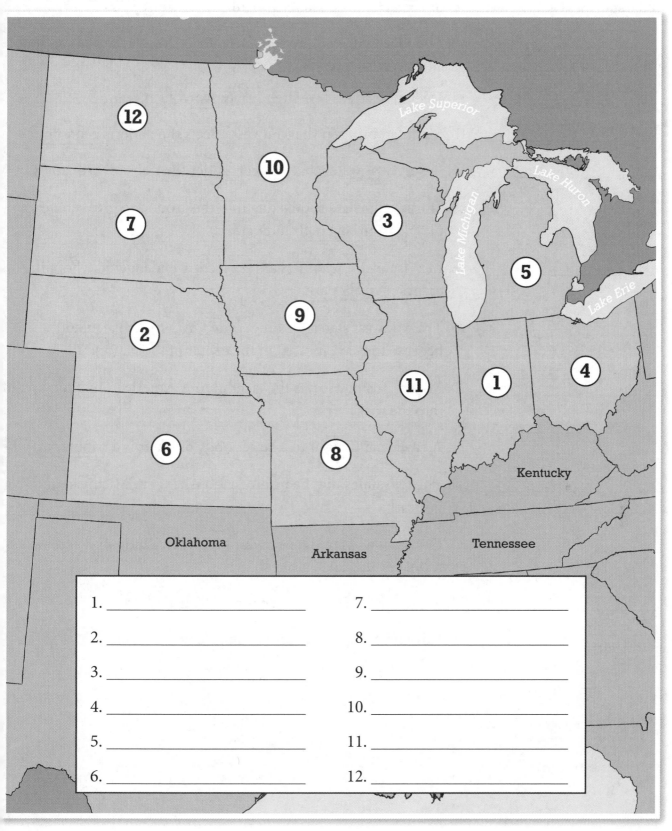

1. _____

2. _____

3. _____

4. _____

5. _____

6. _____

7. _____

8. _____

9. _____

10. _____

11. _____

12. _____

Write *True* if the statement is true.
If the statement is false, write the correction for the underlined word.

_____ 13. The Black Hills of South Dakota are called black because their slopes are covered with <u>coal</u>.

_____ 14. Deciduous trees lose their leaves <u>twice</u> each year.

_____ 15. Manufacturing in the Midwest affects the nation's <u>economy</u>.

_____ 16. Reserves of water that lie deep under the rich soil are <u>canals</u>.

_____ 17. Storm cellars are rooms dug into the ground to give refuge to people from <u>severe thunderstorms</u>.

_____ 18. In Wisconsin, scientists are protecting endangered whooping cranes in a <u>city park</u>.

_____ 19. The Midwest states are often called "America's <u>Farmland</u>" because they are located in the center of the nation.

_____ 20. Mount Rushmore has the faces of four American <u>Indians</u> carved into the rock.

_____ 21. A river that flows into a larger body of water is a <u>tributary</u>.

_____ 22. The two states that lie in "Tornado Alley" are <u>Michigan</u> and Nebraska.

_____ 23. Flat grasslands in the Midwest that receive little rain and have few trees are called a <u>marsh</u>.

_____ 24. Minnesota's Mesabi Range is rich with <u>gold</u> ore.

_____ 25. Farmers can raise crops on <u>arable</u> land.

Industries in the Midwest

Use Student Text pages 345 to 347 to complete the chart.

Industry	Products	
Agriculture	_____ wheat _____ hogs	_____ cherries _____ cranberries
_____	wood	
Manufacturing	_____ _____ equipment aviation equipment	_____ supplies _____ products breakfast _____

List some service industries in the Midwest.

_____

_____

Write one paragraph about a product you would want to produce if you were a farmer in the Midwest. Include reasons for choosing that product.

_____

_____

_____

_____

_____

_____

Cities of the Midwest

Use Student Text pages 348 to 350 to complete the chart.

City	Then	Now	Points of Interest
Cities in the Midwest			
Chicago, Illinois	Much of the city _____ in _____.	The city is famous for buildings such as the _____ Tower and the _____ Building.	home of the first _____ in the world; sports teams; museums; concerts; Navy Pier
Detroit, Michigan	first settled by the _____; prospered because of automobile _____ until the 1970s	City and state _____ are working to help Detroit again become a _____ city in the region.	sports teams; _____ Museum; Greenfield Village
Minneapolis, Minnesota	first boomed with _____ and _____ mills	grew together to become the largest _____ area in the United States; called _____ Cities	the _____ of America that has an indoor _____ park; museums; churches; James J. Hill House
Saint Paul, Minnesota	fur trade center		
Saint Louis, Missouri	In 1804 the Lewis and Clark _____ headed into the Louisiana Territory from this city.	called the _____ City	Gateway _____
Cleveland, Ohio	industrial city that _____ during the second half of the 1900s	_____ enjoy visiting its sights.	_____ arenas; the _____ Garden
Cincinnati, Ohio	was the Midwest's center of _____ before Chicago and Saint Louis	People visit the _____ and enjoy the _____.	home of America's first professional _____ team, the _____

Gateway Arch

Research the Gateway Arch in Saint Louis, Missouri.
Use the information to complete the sentences.

architect	tallest
clear	thirty
concrete	top
expansion	tram
Mississippi River	United States
monument	1947
Park Rangers	1963
safe	1965
steel	17,246

1. The construction of the Gateway Arch was begun in _____ and completed in _____.

2. The arch was designed by an _____ in _____.

3. It was built as a _____ to the westward _____ of the United States.

4. The arch is 630 feet tall and is the _____ monument in the _____.

5. It is made of _____ and _____ and weighs _____ tons.

6. The _____ flows directly below the arch.

7. Tourists reach the top of the arch by riding a _____.

8. _____ work at the top of the arch to answer questions, help out, and keep people _____.

9. A person can see up to _____ miles in either direction on a _____ day from the _____ of the arch.

Religion of the Region

Match the description with the term.

_____ 1. a Muslim place of worship

_____ 2. often the religion of Irish and Hispanic immigrants

_____ 3. location of the largest American mosque

_____ 4. religion of the settlers along the Great Lakes

_____ 5. widely varied because the Midwest is a land of immigrants

_____ 6. religion of immigrants arriving from Germany and Scandinavia

_____ 7. denominations of most people in the Midwest during the 1800s

A. Catholicism
B. Dearborn, Michigan
C. Dutch Reformed
D. Lutheranism
E. Methodist or Baptist
F. mosque
G. religious beliefs

Answer the questions.

8. Why is the Midwest a wonderful place for those who do not know Christ to learn of Him?

_____

_____

_____

9. How has the Midwest changed politically?

_____

_____

_____

_____

_____

_____

_____

Use the map to write the letter for each state.

_____ 1. Indiana

_____ 2. Nebraska

_____ 3. Wisconsin

_____ 4. Ohio

_____ 5. Michigan

_____ 6. Kansas

_____ 7. South Dakota

_____ 8. Missouri

_____ 9. Iowa

_____ 10. Minnesota

_____ 11. Illinois

_____ 12. North Dakota

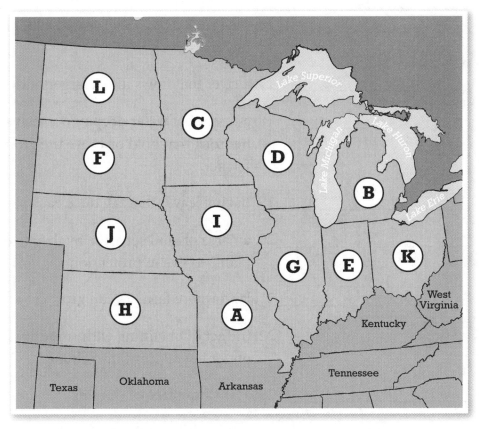

Answer the questions.

13. Why are the states in the Midwest called "America's Heartland"? _____

_____

_____

14. What affects the weather in the Midwest? _____

_____

_____

_____

15. What impact did immigrants have on religious beliefs in the Midwest? _____

_____

_____

_____

Chapter Review

Write the correct term for each definition. Use the Glossary as needed.

_____ 16. flat grasslands in the Midwest that receive little rain and have few trees

_____ 17. a river that flows into a larger body of water

_____ 18. a reserve of water deep under rich soil; layers of sand, gravel, or bedrock that hold or move the ground water, making the soil fertile

_____ 19. having leaves that fall once each year

_____ 20. an area of land set aside by the government for wild animals and plants to live in protection

_____ 21. land where farmers can grow crops

_____ 22. the act of obtaining with some effort or difficulty, as in obtaining oil from the ground

_____ 23. a Muslim place of worship

_____ 24. states whose voting swings back and forth between Republican and Democrat

Write *True* if the statement is true.
If the statement is false, write the correction for the underlined word.

_____ 25. The largest rivers in the Midwest are the Mississippi, the Ohio, and the <u>Missouri</u> Rivers.

_____ 26. Mount Rushmore and an unfinished carving of Crazy Horse are two important memorials found in the <u>Ozark Mountains</u>.

_____ 27. The first <u>Democratic</u> president, Abraham Lincoln, was from the Midwest.

_____ 28. By the late 1800s Chicago became the <u>smallest</u> city in the Midwest.

_____ 29. Successful cities are usually founded near <u>water</u>.

Places to See

The Grand Canyon has been a national park since 1919. Nearly five million people visit the park each year. The most popular place for viewing the canyon is the South Rim. All along this rim of the canyon are overlooks offering views of the colorful rock layers in the canyon walls.

Many visitors explore the canyon by taking mule rides. The mules carry riders along the rim or down into the canyon. Mules are reliable animals for a trail ride. They are less jumpy and more sure-footed than horses. Mules have been taking people down the canyon's Bright Angel Trail since the late 1800s.

Answer the questions.

1. When did the Grand Canyon become a national park? _____

2. How many people visit the park each year? _____

3. What is the most popular place for viewing the canyon? _____

4. What can be found all along the rim of the canyon? _____

5. What do the overlooks allow visitors to do? _____

6. What animals carry riders along the rim or down into the canyon? _____

7. What makes mules reliable animals for a trail ride? _____

_____

8. What is the name of the trail that mules have been taking people down since the late 1800s?

_____

The Southwest Region

Use the Glossary to match the term with the correct definition.

_____ 1. adobe

_____ 2. reservation

_____ 3. Coronado

_____ 4. Dust Bowl

_____ 5. hogan

_____ 6. the Alamo

A. an area of land set aside by the US government for Native Americans

B. a Navajo home that was dome shaped and made of wooden poles, tree bark, and mud

C. a building material made from clay and straw that dries and hardens in the sun

D. a Spanish man who explored much of New Mexico and parts of Arizona

E. a Spanish mission that played an important part in Texas history

F. the term for the damage brought to farmers in the Southwest during the Great Depression and for the area where damage occurred

Answer the questions.

7. How is the Southwest different from the other regions? _____

_____

_____

8. Which Indians often made their homes inside caves in cliffs? _____

9. What is the Spanish word that means "village" or "town"? _____

Describe what happened in the Dust Bowl.

_____

_____

_____

Write the names of the states in the Southwest where they belong on the map.

10. _____

11. _____

12. _____

13. _____

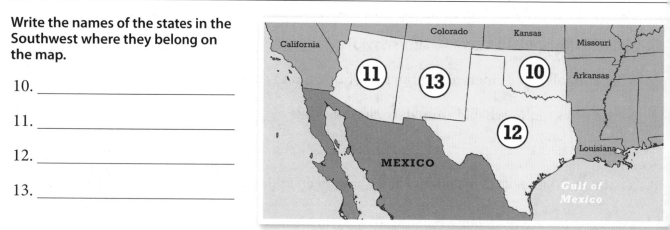

Flora and Fauna

Use the word bank to label the pictures.

armadillo	jackrabbit	saguaro cactus
Gila monster	palo verde	scorpion
Indian blanket	roadrunner	yucca

1. _____

2. _____

3. _____

4. _____

5. _____

6. _____

Complete the sentences using the correct word from the word bank.

7. The _____ is completely green.

8. The _____ is the largest cactus in the United States.

9. The _____ is known for its sharp, spiky green leaves and stalks of white flowers.

10. The _____ flower is red and yellow.

11. The _____ is the largest native lizard in the United States.

12. The _____ is a small mammal with a long tail and an armor-like shell.

13. A _____ runs along on the ground more often than it flies.

14. The sting of the _____ can be quite painful.

Climate in the Southwest

Circle the abbreviations of the Southwest states that apply to the sentence.

AZ   NM   OK   TX   1. Two major deserts cover portions of these states.

AZ   NM   OK   TX   2. This state is shaped like a cooking pan with a long handle.

AZ   NM   OK   TX   3. The Colorado River flows down from the north into this state.

AZ   NM   OK   TX   4. This state's resources include copper and timber.

AZ   NM   OK   TX   5. This state is rich in uranium, salts, and coal.

AZ   NM   OK   TX   6. Parts of these states are humid because of the warm, moist air from the Gulf of Mexico.

AZ   NM   OK   TX   7. This state sometimes experiences hurricanes and tropical storms.

AZ   NM   OK   TX   8. This state's land is a rich source of soil for farming.

AZ   NM   OK   TX   9. This state's resources include oil and natural gas.

AZ   NM   OK   TX   10. This state is usually hot in summer and often experiences tornadoes in the spring.

Answer the questions.

11. How do farmers in Arizona water crops? _____

12. What two deserts cover portions of Arizona, New Mexico, and Texas? _____

_____

13. What does the dry weather in the Southwest often bring? _____

_____

14. What do people love about the Southwest? _____

_____

Write the names of the states in the Southwest where they belong on the map.

1. _____

2. _____

3. _____

4. _____

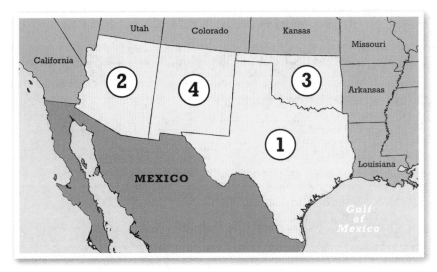

Match the definition with the correct word.

_____ 5. a small hill with steep sides

_____ 6. a rock carving made by ancient people long ago

_____ 7. a hill with a flat top

_____ 8. a Navajo home that was dome shaped and made of wooden poles, tree bark, and mud

_____ 9. the term for the damage brought to farmers in the Southwest during the Great Depression and for the area where damage occurred

_____ 10. an area of land set aside by the US government for Native Americans

_____ 11. a building material made from clay and straw that dries and hardens in the sun

A. adobe
B. butte
C. Dust Bowl
D. hogan
E. mesa
F. petroglyph
G. reservation

Answer the questions.

12. What are the major industries in the Southwest? _____

_____

13. What are some of the favorite tourist sites in the Southwest? _____

_____

14. What Spanish mission played an important part in Texas history? _____

15. What is the largest native lizard in the United States? _____

Major Cities

Mark the city that matches the description.

	Houston	Phoenix	Santa Fe	Oklahoma City
Formed during the Land Rush of 1889				
The largest city in the Southwest				
Called the Valley of the Sun				
Has a national memorial at the location of a former federal building				
Became the capital of a Spanish province in 1610				
Has pueblo-style buildings				
The home of the Johnson Space Center				
Directs river water into canals				

Write the correct answer to complete each sentence.

1. The _____ was built during the Great Depression.

2. Builders took _____ to finish the dam.

3. Wheeler Peak is the _____ in the Southwest.

4. Most of the Indian _____ in the Southwest are in Arizona and New Mexico.

5. Southwest Native American art includes _____, _____, and turquoise _____.

Answer the question.

6. What is the purpose of the Hoover Dam?

_____

_____

Demographics

Write the words to complete the sentences.

1. The Southwest includes only _____ states.

2. The Southwestern states are some of the nation's largest in _____.

3. A large portion of Arizona, Oklahoma, and New Mexico is _____ or _____.

4. Although the main language of the Southwest region is English, many of its people also speak _____.

5. Some public schools in the Southwest have special _____ that allow students to learn in Spanish.

6. Oklahoma is the strongest "_____ state" in the region.

7. Oklahoma has voted for a _____ for president in nearly every election of the last fifty years.

8. The influence of the early Spanish Catholic _____ is still strong in the Southwest.

9. The people in the Church of Jesus Christ of Latter-day Saints are also known as _____.

10. Mormons spread out into several states in the West and Southwest. This area is called the _____.

11. Believers in the Southwest must drive many miles to attend solid Bible-preaching _____.

12. Children, teens, and adults can visit Christian _____ in the Southwest and enjoy nature and outdoor sports and learn more about God.

Match the words with the correct phrase.

_____ 1. Hoover Dam

_____ 2. Wheeler Peak

_____ 3. Petrified Forest

_____ 4. Painted Desert

_____ 5. Grand Canyon

_____ 6. the Alamo

_____ 7. Carlsbad Caverns

A. caves in New Mexico where evening visitors can watch thousands of bats leave to hunt for food

B. formed as a result of the Flood

C. puts the water of the Colorado River to use

D. has fossils of fallen trees and also has rock carvings

E. played an important part in Texas history

F. the highest point in the Southwest

G. contains colorful rocks

Mark the correct city in the Southwest.

8. Which is the largest city in the Southwest?
   ○ Oklahoma City
   ○ Phoenix
   ○ Houston
   ○ Santa Fe

9. Which city in the Southwest is called the Valley of the Sun?
   ○ Oklahoma City
   ○ Phoenix
   ○ Houston
   ○ Santa Fe

10. Which city is known as the Horse Show Capital of the World?
    ○ Oklahoma City
    ○ Phoenix
    ○ Houston
    ○ Santa Fe

11. Which city in the Southwest was formed during the Land Rush of 1889?
    ○ Oklahoma City
    ○ Phoenix
    ○ Houston
    ○ Santa Fe

Use the Glossary to write the definition.

12. butte _____

_____

13. mesa _____

_____

14. hogan _____

_____

15. reservation _____

_____

16. petroglyph _____

_____

17. adobe _____

_____

18. pueblo _____

_____

Answer the questions.

19. How is the Southwest different from the other regions? _____

_____

_____

20. What happened to the Southwest during the Dust Bowl? _____

_____

_____

_____

Fill in the names of the states.

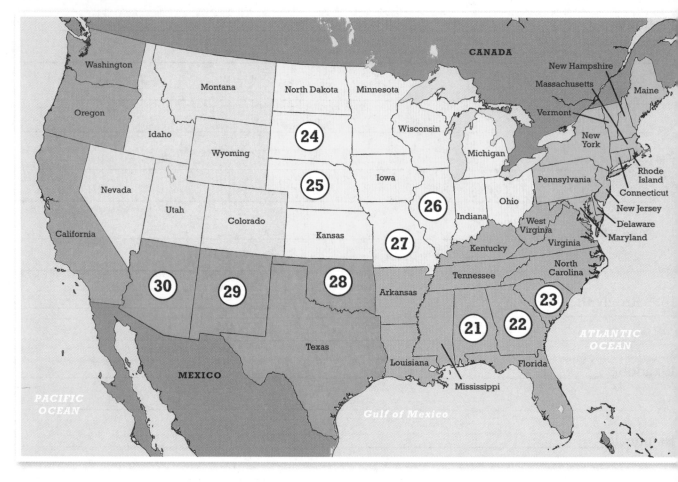

21. _____   26. _____

22. _____   27. _____

23. _____   28. _____

24. _____   29. _____

25. _____   30. _____

Yellowstone National Park, located in parts of Wyoming, Montana, and Idaho, was America's first national park. Established in 1872, Yellowstone has mountains, rivers, canyons, and lakes. It also has a wide variety of wildlife. Bears, wolves, bison, elk, and moose live there. Many kinds of birds, fish, and reptiles can also be found in the park.

Some of the famous features of the park are its geysers and hot springs. A geyser erupts when the hot water underground is exposed to increasing pressure. The geyser then releases steam into the air like a teapot. More than half the geysers in the world are found in Yellowstone National Park. The most famous geyser is called Old Faithful because it erupts on a fairly regular schedule. Visitors can be almost certain to see Old Faithful erupt at least once every ninety minutes.

Fill in the blanks with the answers to the clues. The shaded letters will spell the name of an animal in Yellowstone National Park that is not mentioned in the article.

1. Old Faithful erupts on a fairly regular ____ ____ ____ ____ ____ ____ ____.

2. Yellowstone National Park is located in parts of Wyoming, Montana,

   and ____ ____ ____ ____ ____.

3. Hot water underground that is exposed to increasing pressure causes

   a ____ ____ ____ ____ ____ ____ to erupt.

4. Another famous feature of the park besides its geysers is the ____ ____ ____

   ____ ____ ____ ____ ____ ____.

5. America's first national park was ____ ____ ____ ____ ____ ____ ____ ____ ____ ____
   National Park.

6. Mammals, birds, fish, and ____ ____ ____ ____ ____ ____ ____ ____ can be found in the park.

Write the shaded letters from above to find the name of another animal that lives in Yellowstone National Park.

____ ____ ____ ____ ____ ____

Write the correct name or term for each description.

_____ 1. a person with no permanent home who moves from place to place in search of food and water

_____ 2. people who built their homes of clay on the mountain ledges

_____ 3. Indian tribes that were nomads

_____

_____

_____ 4. the first European explorers to investigate what is now Utah and Nevada

_____ 5. the area that became the property of the United States in 1803

_____ 6. the first Americans to travel through the Rocky Mountain area

_____

_____ 7. a gap between two mountains that makes them easier to get through

_____ 8. the gap between mountains in Wyoming that allowed pioneers to travel to Oregon and California in wagon trains

_____ 9. the most famous fight brought about by the moving of Americans onto Indian lands

Flora and Fauna

Write the words to complete the sentences.

_____ 1. The most common tree in the Rocky Mountains is the ____.

_____ 2. The longest-living kind of tree in the United States is the ____.

_____ 3. The trees that add fall color to the mountainsides are the ____

_____ and ____.

_____ 4. The most common color of the ____ is blue with a white center.

_____ 5. The ____ paintbrush has the appearance of an artist's brush that has been dipped in paint.

Complete the chart.

Fauna in the Rocky Mountain Region			
Large animals in the mountains	Large animals in the flatlands	Smaller animals and reptiles	Fish
_____	_____	_____	_____
_____	_____	_____	_____
_____	_____	_____	_____
_____	_____	_____	_____
_____	_____	_____	_____
_____	_____	_____	_____
_____	_____	_____	_____

The Nature of the Place

Match the description with the correct term.

_____ 1. runs through the Rocky Mountains

_____ 2. the flat area west of the Rocky Mountains

_____ 3. the wide-open flatlands east of the Rocky Mountains

_____ 4. some of the tallest mountains in the United States

_____ 5. a cold area on tall mountains where no trees grow

A. Great Basin
B. Great Plains
C. Rocky Mountains
D. tundra
E. western Continental Divide

Refer to Student Text pages 385–88 to complete each statement.

6. The Great Basin is in _____ and western _____.

7. The climate in the Great Basin is _____.

8. The _____ of Montana and Wyoming support herds of _____ and _____.

9. The eastern parts of Colorado, Wyoming, and Montana are part of the _____.

10. The _____ gets its name because the water that flows into it never reaches the Pacific.

Write the names of the states in the Rocky Mountain region.

11. _____

12. _____

13. _____

14. _____

15. _____

16. _____

The western Continental Divide splits North America into two main areas. On one side rivers flow west to the Pacific Ocean. On the other side rivers flow east to the Gulf of Mexico.

_____

Use the Glossary to define each term.

1. nomad _____

   _____

2. pass _____

   _____

3. tundra _____

   _____

4. arid _____

   _____

5. rain shadow _____

   _____

6. Continental Divide _____

   _____

Complete the statements.

7. The _____ _____ are a major mountain range in the

   _____ United States.

8. The first European explorers to investigate what is now Utah and Nevada were the

   _____ in _____.

9. The discovery of _____ in Wyoming by a group of _____

   allowed _____ to travel to Oregon and California in wagon trains.

Write *True* if the statement is true.
If the statement is false, write the correction for the underlined word.

_____ 10. The most common tree in the Rocky Mountains is the cottonwood.

_____ 11. The Nevada state tree is the bristlecone pine.

_____ 12. The state flower of Colorado is the columbine.

_____ 13. Elk, moose, and wolves stay mostly in the mountains.

_____ 14. Poisonous reptiles in this region include the rattlesnake and the pika.

Answer the questions.

15. What is an area in the arctic region where only small shrubs, mosses, and grasses can grow?

_____

16. What are the wide-open flatlands east of the Rocky Mountains called?

_____

17. What is the area where the Great Salt Lake is located called?

_____

18. What is the term for an area that receives very little rain due to a mountain barrier that causes the wind to lose moisture? _____

19. What important natural resource do many locations in the West lack? _____

List industries found in the Rocky Mountain region.

Industries in the Rocky Mountain Region

_____	_____
_____	_____
_____	_____
_____	_____
_____	_____
_____	_____
_____	_____

Write _ID_ for Idaho, _MT_ for Montana, _WY_ for Wyoming, _CO_ for Colorado, _UT_ for Utah, or _NV_ for Nevada for each description. (Answers will be used only once.)

_____ 1. Banking and other service industries are important in Nevada as well as in this state.

_____ 2. Potatoes, wheat, and sugar beets are the most important crops raised in this state.

_____ 3. Cattle ranching is this state's biggest business.

_____ 4. Jobs in this state include growing wheat, barley, hay, and sugar beets in addition to cattle ranching, mining, lumberjack work, and tourism.

_____ 5. Printing books, making food, and gambling are sources of work in this state.

_____ 6. Jobs in this state include ranching, mining, tourism, real estate, manufacturing, communications, and medicine.

Mark all the correct answers.

1. What city is called the Mile High City because it is about one mile above sea level?
   - ○ Las Vegas
   - ○ Denver
   - ○ Salt Lake City
   - ○ Cheyenne

2. Which groups of people have lived in the Rocky Mountain states over the years?
   - ○ people from all over
   - ○ cliff dwellers
   - ○ Mormons
   - ○ nomadic Indians

3. Which characteristics describe many people in this region?
   - ○ agree on religion
   - ○ like outdoor activities
   - ○ need to hear the gospel
   - ○ have an independent streak

4. What is true of the Mormons?
   - ○ influenced Utah and Idaho
   - ○ attend religious services rarely
   - ○ attend Christian churches
   - ○ attend religious services regularly

5. What outdoor activities are enjoyed in this region?
   - ○ mountain climbing
   - ○ hiking
   - ○ skiing
   - ○ fishing and hunting

6. What makes it difficult to start Christian churches in this region?
   - ○ There are too many Christian churches.
   - ○ Mormons are often very committed to remaining Mormons.
   - ○ People in these states sometimes live great distances apart.
   - ○ In some of these states, people do not want much to do with religion.

Write the names of the states in the Rocky Mountain region.

7. _____

8. _____

9. _____

10. _____

11. _____

12. _____

Chapter Review

Match the description with the correct term.

_____ 1. built their homes of clay into mountain ledges

_____ 2. gave their name to the state of Utah

_____ 3. a person with no permanent home who moves from place to place in search of food and water

_____ 4. the first European explorers to investigate what is now Utah and Nevada

_____ 5. the parts of Colorado, Wyoming, and Montana that became property of the United States in 1803

_____ 6. the first Americans to travel through parts of Colorado, Wyoming, and Montana

_____ 7. enabled pioneers to travel to Oregon and California in wagon trains

_____ 8. led the Mormons across the West to live in Utah

_____ 9. most famous fight brought about by the moving of Americans onto Indian lands

A. Battle of the Little Bighorn
B. Brigham Young
C. Lewis and Clark
D. Louisiana Purchase
E. nomad
F. Pueblo Indians
G. South Pass
H. the Spanish
I. Ute Indians

Use the Glossary to define each term.

10. lumberjack _____

_____

11. fourteeners _____

_____

12. Mountain Standard Time Zone _____

_____

Match the description with the correct term.

_____ 13. an area where there is very little rain due to a mountain barrier that causes the wind to lose moisture

_____ 14. mountains extending from Alaska to Mexico, mostly in the Rocky Mountains, from which the river water flows out in two different directions

_____ 15. an area in the arctic region where only small shrubs, mosses, and grasses can grow

_____ 16. important natural resource that many locations in the West lack

_____ 17. famous mountain that is often visited in Colorado

_____ 18. flat area to the west of the Rocky Mountains

_____ 19. largest saltwater lake in North and South America

A. Continental Divide
B. Great Basin
C. Great Salt Lake
D. Pikes Peak
E. rain shadow
F. tundra
G. water

Fill in the states of the Rocky Mountain region.

20. _____

21. _____

22. _____

23. _____

24. _____

25. _____

Places to See

Read the article and answer the questions.

Mount Saint Helens is a volcano located in the state of Washington. On March 27, 1980, the volcano erupted for the first time in more than 100 years. Small eruptions continued during the next two months. Then on May 18, an earthquake caused a huge eruption. The top of the volcano crumbled in an avalanche. Wind and hot pumice destroyed many square miles of the land around the mountain. A cloud of ash rose thousands of feet in the air and then covered much of the surrounding forest. Fifty-seven people lost their lives.

After the eruption, the US government created the Mount Saint Helens National Volcanic Monument. The monument is made up of 110,000 acres of land. This land is managed by forest service workers. Scientists conduct research in the area. Many visitors also come to learn more about Mount Saint Helens or to hike, climb, and camp. Creationary scientists tell us that Mount Saint Helens proves that rock layers can be formed quickly. Millions of years are not necessary for rock layers to be created.

1. Where is Mount Saint Helens located? _____

2. What happened on March 27, 1980? _____

_____

3. What happened on May 18? _____

4. What destroyed many square miles of the land around the mountain? _____

_____

5. What rose and covered much of the forest surrounding the mountain? _____

6. What is the name of the monument? _____

_____

7. What can visitors do at the monument? _____

_____

8. What do creationary scientists tell us that Mount Saint Helens proves? _____

_____

The Pacific States

Match the description with the correct term.

_____ 1. were the first people to live in Hawaii

_____ 2. joined the United States in the mid-1800s

_____ 3. were good spots to settle because of the rich soil

_____ 4. was the first European to see the Hawaiian islands

_____ 5. became the fiftieth state

_____ 6. were Alaska's native people

> A. Washington
> B. Hawaii
> C. Polynesians
> D. volcanic islands
> E. Eskimos and Russians
> F. James Cook

Answer the questions.

7. What do all the Pacific states have in common? _____

8. How do the states in this region differ from states in other regions? _____

_____

9. Which two Indian tribes lived in California? _____

10. Where did the Spanish settle? _____

11. What did the Spanish priests build? _____

12. What did the Spanish priests want to do? _____

13. When did people from Asia and Latin America move to California? _____

14. What three groups settled in the northwestern Pacific region in the 1800s? _____

_____

_____

Write the names of the Pacific states.

15. _____

16. _____

17. _____

18. _____

19. _____

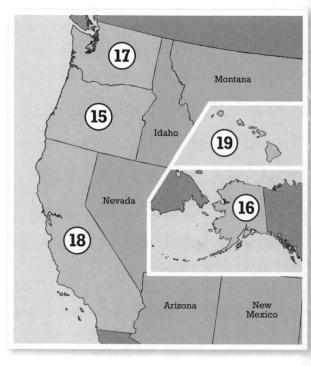

Flora and Fauna

Label the pictures using the word bank.

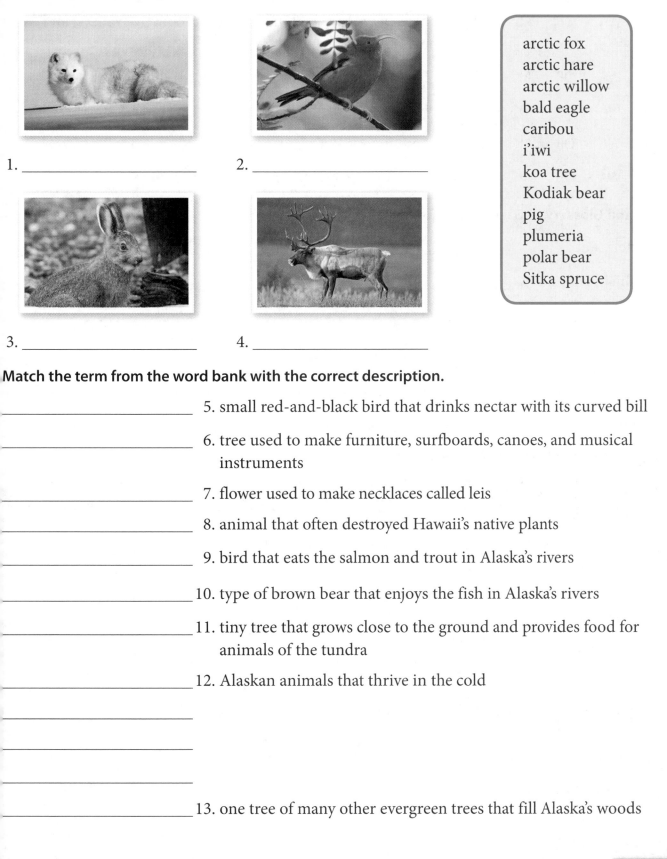

1. _____   2. _____

arctic fox
arctic hare
arctic willow
bald eagle
caribou
i'iwi
koa tree
Kodiak bear
pig
plumeria
polar bear
Sitka spruce

3. _____   4. _____

Match the term from the word bank with the correct description.

_____ 5. small red-and-black bird that drinks nectar with its curved bill

_____ 6. tree used to make furniture, surfboards, canoes, and musical instruments

_____ 7. flower used to make necklaces called leis

_____ 8. animal that often destroyed Hawaii's native plants

_____ 9. bird that eats the salmon and trout in Alaska's rivers

_____ 10. type of brown bear that enjoys the fish in Alaska's rivers

_____ 11. tiny tree that grows close to the ground and provides food for animals of the tundra

_____ 12. Alaskan animals that thrive in the cold

_____
_____
_____

_____ 13. one tree of many other evergreen trees that fill Alaska's woods

Geography and Resources

Circle all the Pacific state abbreviations to which each sentence applies.

HI   WA   OR   AK   CA   1. These states have high mountains, productive valleys, and beautiful coastlines.

HI   WA   OR   AK   CA   2. This state is famous for its volcanoes and beaches.

HI   WA   OR   AK   CA   3. This state has the highest mountain in North America.

HI   WA   OR   AK   CA   4. These states share similar landscapes.

HI   WA   OR   AK   CA   5. This state's geography creates climate extremes.

Use the Glossary or Gazetteer to define each term.

6. dormant _____

7. shield volcano _____

_____

8. Mount McKinley _____

9. glacier _____

10. archipelago _____

List resources and products of each state.

Alaska	California	Hawaii	Oregon	Washington

HERITAGE STUDIES

Write the names of the Pacific states.

1. _____

2. _____

3. _____

4. _____

5. _____

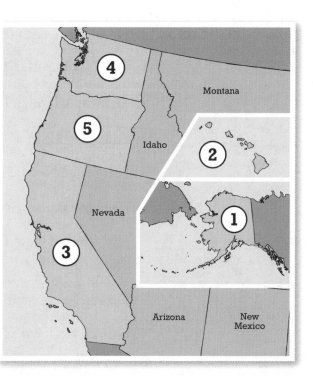

Match the terms with the definitions.

_____ 6. archipelago

_____ 7. deciduous

_____ 8. dormant

_____ 9. glacier

_____ 10. lumber

_____ 11. shield volcano

_____ 12. tech industry

A. river of ice that is formed by tightly packed snow
B. an island group or chain of islands
C. being inactive for a period of time
D. a service industry that includes computer design and programming
E. having leaves that fall once each year
F. a type of volcano that produces slow-flowing, runny lava and rarely erupts violently
G. timber sawed into boards to make useful wood products, such as houses, paper, cardboard, and furniture

Answer the questions.

13. What is the highest mountain in North America? _____

14. What are the major industries in the Pacific states that deal with getting raw materials?

_____

15. What are some industries that turn raw materials into a more complete product? _____

_____

16. What are some of the service industries in the Pacific states? _____

_____

Write the name of the correct city.

_____ 1. This city is America's second-largest city.

_____ 2. Alcatraz Island, a former prison, is in the bay of this city.

_____ 3. This city began as a railroad station and port.

_____ 4. The Space Needle in this city stands 600 feet high.

_____ 5. This city sits across the Columbia River from Fort Vancouver.

_____ 6. The Golden Gate Bridge connects this city to the rest of California.

_____ 7. This city was rebuilt after an earthquake in 1964.

_____ 8. This city is located on the island of Oahu.

_____ 9. The bones of saber-toothed cats are on display at the Page Museum in this city.

_____ 10. This city has the only major-league baseball and football teams in the American Northwest.

_____ 11. Its nickname is the City of Roses.

_____ 12. This city is known for Chinatown, streetcars, and the Fisherman's Wharf.

_____ 13. People can visit the Pearl Harbor Memorial in this city.

Demographics

Write the words that complete each sentence.

_____ 1. Americans of many _____ live in the Pacific states.

_____ 2. All five Pacific states have large populations of people with _____ ancestry.

_____ 3. The Pacific states enjoy a wide _____ of people and cultures.

_____ 4. California's location encourages immigrants from _____ to settle there.

_____ 5. This mixture of cultures can remind Americans that their nation is sometimes called a _____.

_____ 6. Because of its location and resources, more people live in _____ than in any other American state.

_____ 7. The Pacific states are more alike in their _____ than in their cultures.

_____ 8. Most voters in the Pacific states normally support the _____ Party.

_____ 9. These Democratic voters want the government to make many _____.

_____ 10. Alaskans usually vote for _____.

_____ 11. Probably the most famous politician from the Pacific states was _____.

_____ 12. These states have a _____ of religious beliefs.

_____ 13. Few people regularly attend _____.

_____ 14. Many people in this region believe that there is no _____.

Chapter Review

Mark all the correct answers.

1. Which became the fiftieth state in 1959?
   - ○ Alaska
   - ○ California
   - ○ Oregon
   - ○ Hawaii

2. Which term describes a tree whose leaves fall once each year?
   - ○ archipelago
   - ○ dormant
   - ○ lumber
   - ○ deciduous

3. Which term describes a volcano that is inactive for a period of time?
   - ○ archipelago
   - ○ dormant
   - ○ shield
   - ○ deciduous

4. What produces slow-flowing, runny lava and rarely erupts violently?
   - ○ shield volcano
   - ○ glacier
   - ○ volcano
   - ○ archipelago

5. What is a river of ice that is formed by tightly packed snow called?
   - ○ shield volcano
   - ○ glacier
   - ○ volcano
   - ○ archipelago

6. What is an island group or chain of islands called?
   - ○ shield volcano
   - ○ glacier
   - ○ archipelago
   - ○ volcano

7. Where is the highest mountain in North America?
   - ○ Alaska
   - ○ Washington
   - ○ Oregon
   - ○ California

8. What are some industries that turn raw materials into a more complete product?
   - ○ education
   - ○ food processing
   - ○ lumber
   - ○ government

9. What are some of the service industries in the Pacific states?
   - ○ tech industry
   - ○ producing electronic equipment
   - ○ tourism
   - ○ medicine

Answer the questions.

10. What term is used to describe a mixture of cultures? _____

_____

11. What major industries in the Pacific states deal with getting raw materials? _____

_____

12. What happened to Mount Saint Helens in 1980? _____

_____

13. Which area of California has companies that write computer programs and apps? _____

_____

14. Who was probably the most famous politician from the Pacific states? _____

_____

15. What two things encourage more people to live in California than in any other American

state? _____

16. What is religion like in the Pacific states? _____

_____

Write the name of the city based on the description.

_____ 17. America's second-largest city

_____ 18. known for the Golden Gate Bridge

_____ 19. began as a railroad station and port

_____ 20. known for the Space Needle

_____ 21. nicknamed the City of Roses

_____ 22. known for the Pearl Harbor Memorial

Fill in the names of the states.

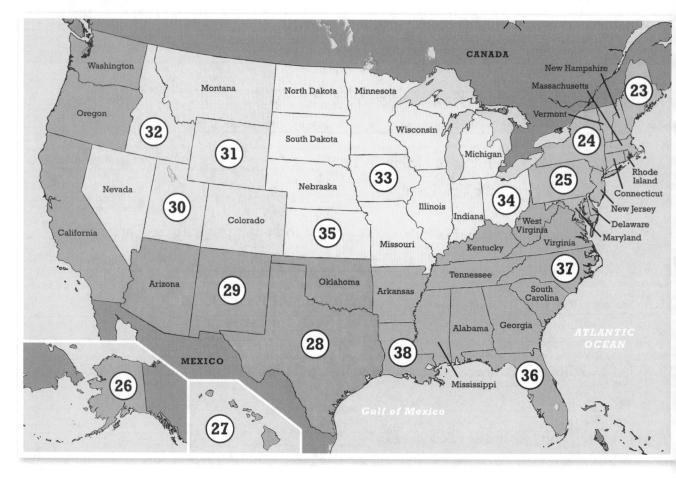

23. _____

24. _____

25. _____

26. _____

27. _____

28. _____

29. _____

30. _____

31. _____

32. _____

33. _____

34. _____

35. _____

36. _____

37. _____

38. _____

Read the article and answer the questions.

The National War Dog Memorial is located on Naval Base Guam, a US naval base on the west harbor of Guam. The memorial honors the dogs who served the US Marine Corps and lost their lives during World War II. These military dogs had various jobs in the war. They explored caves, sniffed out explosives, and acted as guards at night while marines were sleeping. Some dogs also carried messages or medical supplies across enemy lines.

The black granite memorial has a large bronze statue of a Doberman pinscher on top of it. It has the inscription *Semper Fidelis* ("Always Faithful"). The memorial then lists the names of twenty-five dogs, such as Tubby, Prince, and Skipper, who were killed in action. Most of these dogs are buried near the memorial. The list of names is followed by the statement that the memorial is given on behalf of the men who worked with these dogs. Many of these men "owe their lives to the bravery and sacrifice of these gallant animals."

1. Where is the National War Dog Memorial located? _____

2. What is the importance of the memorial? _____

_____

3. What were some of the jobs of the dogs? _____

_____

_____

4. What does the memorial look like? _____

_____

5. What is the inscription? _____

6. How many names of dogs are listed on the memorial? _____

7. Where are most of the dogs buried? _____

8. Who wanted the memorial? _____

Puerto Rico

Write *L* if the statement tells how the territories are like the fifty states.
Write *U* if the statement tells how they are unlike the fifty states.

_____ 1. People who live in territories are United States nationals.

_____ 2. The people in territories do not vote in national elections.

_____ 3. In some territories the residents are US citizens at birth.

_____ 4. People in all territories enjoy the protection of the US government and can serve in the US military.

_____ 5. In Congress, representatives from territories do not have the same voting rights as representatives from states do.

_____ 6. People in territories use the US postal system and can travel back and forth to the states without a passport.

Complete the sentences.

7. Puerto Rico is an island in the _____ southeast of Florida.

8. The name *Puerto Rico* is Spanish for "_____."

9. The _____ were some of the earliest people to live in Puerto Rico.

10. The Spanish brought _____ to the island to help produce crops.

11. In the 1950s Puerto Rico became a _____.

12. _____ influence can be seen in Puerto Rico's music, literature, and art.

13. The largest religion on the island is _____.

14. Puerto Rico produces electronics, _____, and machines.

15. A tree frog called a _____ is named after the sound it makes.

Match the terms with the correct description.

A. a danger to the US Virgin Islands, especially during June through November

B. a group of three main islands just east of Puerto Rico in the Caribbean Sea

C. beautiful hills and valleys, beaches, and coral reefs

D. yellow trumpetbush

E. a large portion of the island of Saint John

F. people groups of the US Virgin Islands

G. Caribs and Arawaks

H. small islands that surround the US Virgin Islands

I. two major religious groups in the US Virgin Islands

J. location of a large oil-refining industry

_____ 1. US Virgin Islands

_____ 2. hurricanes

_____ 3. African, American, Latin American, and Asian

_____ 4. official flower of the territory

_____ 5. Roman Catholics and Protestant Christians

_____ 6. early settlers

_____ 7. a national park

_____ 8. natural resources

_____ 9. cays

_____ 10. Saint Croix

Coral Reef

Coral reefs are found in or near the tropics in the ocean. They are formed by animals called coral that live in the warm salt water of the tropics. Certain types of coral take salt from the ocean water and use it to build limestone skeletons that form the reefs. Many visitors to the Northern Mariana Islands like to go snorkeling around the coral reefs to see the variety of fish and plants that live there.

Draw a picture of a coral reef.

_____

Write the correct term for the definition.

> cays   hurricanes   rain shadow
> Chamorros   Mariana Trench   red-flowering flame tree
> commonwealth   Puerto Rico   territories

_____ 1. the official tree of the Northern Mariana Islands

_____ 2. a nation or state governed by the people

_____ 3. "rich port"

_____ 4. a danger to the US Virgin Islands, especially during June through November

_____ 5. early settlers on the Northern Mariana Islands

_____ 6. other lands belonging to the United States in addition to the fifty states

_____ 7. the result when mountains block most of the rainfall

_____ 8. small islands that surround the US Virgin Islands

_____ 9. the deepest point in the world's oceans

Circle PR for Puerto Rico, USVI for US Virgin Islands, or NMI for Northern Mariana Islands.

PR   USVI   NMI   10. The Taíno Indians were some of the earliest people to live here.

PR   USVI   NMI   11. Ferdinand Magellan found these islands in 1521.

PR   USVI   NMI   12. This territory is a group of three main islands just east of Puerto Rico in the Caribbean Sea.

PR   USVI   NMI   13. The capital is located on Saipan.

PR   USVI   NMI   14. This territory produces electronics, medicines, and machines.

PR   USVI   NMI   15. The clothing industry is important in these islands.

PR   USVI   NMI   16. A national park is located in this territory.

Mark all the correct answers.

1. Which territory is one of the Mariana Islands?
   - ○ US Virgin Islands
   - ○ Puerto Rico
   - ○ Guam

2. Which country controlled Guam for more than three centuries?
   - ○ Spain
   - ○ France
   - ○ Denmark

3. What does the Chamorro culture value?
   - ○ native music
   - ○ native foods
   - ○ native legends

4. What are the tall stone pillars from ancient Chamorro buildings called?
   - ○ boundary stones
   - ○ old stones
   - ○ latte stones

5. What does the phrase "Hafa adai!" mean?
   - ○ How are you, friend?
   - ○ Good day to you, friend!
   - ○ Have a nice day!

6. Which two religious groups are important on the island?
   - ○ Roman Catholics
   - ○ Protestant Christians
   - ○ Mormons

7. What affects the weather on Guam?
   - ○ temperature
   - ○ ocean currents
   - ○ sea winds

8. What hurricane-like storm sometimes threatens Guam?
   - ○ typhoon
   - ○ earthquake
   - ○ flood

9. What are Guam's natural resources?
   - ○ fish
   - ○ other ocean wildlife
   - ○ gold

10. What is the official tree of Guam?
    - ○ coconut palm
    - ○ fir
    - ○ ifit

11. Which flowering plant has long, sharp thorns?
    - ○ black-eyed Susan
    - ○ daisy
    - ○ bougainvillea

12. Which snake has become a problem for Guam?
    - ○ brown tree snake
    - ○ python
    - ○ black snake

13. What are important industries on Guam?
    - ○ tourism
    - ○ US military
    - ○ construction

American Samoa

Write *True* if the statement is true.
If the statement is false, write the correction for the underlined words.

_____ 1. The Samoan Islands are a chain of islands in the <u>Atlantic</u> Ocean.

_____ 2. An <u>atoll</u> is a ring-shaped island made of coral.

_____ 3. <u>John Williams</u> was the leader of the British missionaries who visited the islands of Samoa in the 1830s.

_____ 4. The Samoan Islands became a US <u>territory</u> in 1900.

_____ 5. Some Samoans served as <u>sailors</u> during World War II.

Write the words to complete the sentences.

_____ 6. Children wear white clothing and perform songs and plays in church services on a holiday called ____.

_____ 7. Over 90 percent of the people in American Samoa are ____.

_____ 8. Samoans greet each other by saying ____.

_____ 9. The main religion in the islands is still ____.

_____ 10. One of the best natural harbors in the Pacific Ocean is found in ____.

_____ 11. Baskets, mats, and grass skirts are made from ____ leaves.

Write one paragraph describing the family in American Samoan culture.

_____

_____

_____

_____

_____

_____

A Good Citizen

List two ways you can be a good citizen of your community.

1. _____

2. _____

Make a prayer list to use as you pray for leaders and people in your community.

1. _____

_____

2. _____

_____

3. _____

_____

4. _____

_____

5. _____

_____

6. _____

_____

7. _____

_____

List things you can do to help people in your community.

1. _____

_____

2. _____

_____

3. _____

_____

4. _____

_____

5. _____

_____

6. _____

_____

7. _____

_____

Match the words with the correct description.

_____ 1. "rich port"

_____ 2. cays

_____ 3. typhoon

_____ 4. atoll

_____ 5. latte stones

_____ 6. Christianity

_____ 7. rain shadow

_____ 8. US Virgin Islands

_____ 9. John Williams

A. small islands that surround the US Virgin Islands

B. Puerto Rico

C. a group of three main islands just east of Puerto Rico in the Caribbean Sea

D. a ring-shaped island made of coral

E. the result when mountains block most of the rainfall

F. a hurricane-like storm that sometimes threatens Guam

G. the main religion in American Samoa

H. leader of British missionaries who visited American Samoa

I. tall stone pillars from ancient Chamorro buildings

Answer the questions.

10. What are two ways you can be a good citizen of your community? _____

_____

11. Who were early settlers of the US Virgin Islands? _____

12. What animal in Puerto Rico is named after the sound it makes? _____

13. Which island in the US Virgin Islands has a large oil-refining industry? _____

14. What does the Chamorro culture in Guam value? _____

_____

15. What is the capital of the Northern Mariana Islands? _____

Mark the territory that matches the description.

		Puerto Rico	US Virgin Islands	Northern Mariana Islands	Guam	American Samoa
16.	Its capital city has one of the best natural harbors in the Pacific Ocean.					
17.	Its capital is located on Saipan.					
18.	The yellow trumpetbush is the official flower.					
19.	It produces electronics, medicines, and machines.					
20.	The official tree of the territory is the ifit.					
21.	It celebrates a holiday called White Sunday.					
22.	The red-flowering flame tree is the official tree of this commonwealth.					
23.	Ferdinand Magellan found the islands in 1521.					

Answer the questions.

24. What is a territory? _____

25. In what ways are territories like the fifty states? _____

_____

_____

_____

26. In what ways are territories unlike the fifty states? _____

_____

_____

_____

I know that my race must change. We cannot hold our own with the white men as we are. We only ask an even chance to live as other men live. We ask to be recognized as men. We ask that the same law shall work alike on all men. If an Indian breaks the law, punish him by the law. If a white man breaks the law, punish him also.

Let me be a free man, free to travel, free to stop, free to work, free to trade where I choose, free to choose my own teachers, free to follow the religion of my fathers, free to talk, think, and act for myself—and I will obey every law or submit to the penalty.

Whenever the white man treats the Indian as they treat each other, then we shall have no more wars.

Joseph, Young, Chief of the Nez Perces; Hare, W. H., Right Rev., D. D. "An Indian's Views of Indian Affairs." *The North American Review* 0128, no. 269 (April 1879): 433.

"The Ninety and Nine"

There were ninety and nine that safely lay
In the shelter of the fold.
But one was out on the hills away,
Far off from the gates of gold.
Away on the mountains wild and bare.
Away from the tender Shepherd's care.
Away from the tender Shepherd's care.

"Lord, Thou hast here Thy ninety and nine;
Are they not enough for Thee?"
But the Shepherd made answer: "This of Mine
Has wandered away from Me;
And although the road be rough and steep,
I go to the desert to find My sheep,
I go to the desert to find My sheep."

But none of the ransomed ever knew
How deep were the waters crossed;
Nor how dark was the night the Lord passed through
Ere He found His sheep that was lost.
Out in the desert He heard its cry,
Sick and helpless and ready to die;
Sick and helpless and ready to die.

"Lord, whence are those blood drops all the way
That mark out the mountain's track?"
"They were shed for one who had gone astray
Ere the Shepherd could bring him back."
"Lord, whence are Thy hands so rent and torn?"
"They are pierced tonight by many a thorn;
They are pierced tonight by many a thorn."

And all through the mountains, thunder riven
And up from the rocky steep,
There arose a glad cry to the gate of Heaven,
"Rejoice! I have found My sheep!"
And the angels echoed around the throne,
"Rejoice, for the Lord brings back His own!
Rejoice, for the Lord brings back His own!"

Music by Ira D. Sankey, words by Elizabeth C. Clephane, "The Ninety and Nine," *Sacred Songs and Solos*, score, 1874 .

Work in the coal breakers is exceedingly hard and dangerous. Crouched over the chutes, the boys sit hour after hour, picking out the pieces of slate and other refuse from the coal as it rushes past to the washers. From the cramped position they have to assume, most of them become more or less deformed and bent-backed like old men. . . . I once stood in a breaker for half an hour and tried to do the work a twelve-year-old boy was doing day after day, for ten hours at a stretch, for sixty cents a day. The gloom of the breaker appalled me. Outside the sun shone brightly, the air was pellucid [clear], and the birds sang in chorus with the trees and the rivers. Within the breaker there was blackness, clouds of deadly dust enfolded everything, the harsh, grinding roar of the machinery and the ceaseless rushing of coal through the chutes filled the ears. I tried to pick out the pieces of slate from the hurrying stream of coal, often missing them; my hands were bruised and cut in a few minutes; I was covered from head to foot with coal dust, and for many hours afterwards I was expectorating some of the small particles of anthracite I had swallowed.

I could not do that work and live, but there were boys of ten and twelve years of age doing it for fifty and sixty cents a day.

Spargo, John. *The Bitter Cry of the Children*. New York: The MacMillan Company, 1915.

Selections from "Request for Declaration of War" (April 2, 1917)

On April 2, 1917, President Woodrow Wilson gave a speech before Congress to ask for a declaration of war against Germany. In a famous line from the speech, he expressed his desire that the world "be made safe for democracy."

The world must be made safe for democracy. Its peace must be planted upon the tested foundations of political liberty. We have no selfish ends to serve. We desire no conquest, no dominion (rule). We seek no indemnities (money paid back for a loss) for ourselves, no material compensation for the sacrifices we shall freely make. We are but one of the champions of the rights of mankind. We shall be satisfied when those rights have been made as secure as the faith and the freedom of nations can make them. . . .

It is a fearful thing to lead this great peaceful people into war, into the most terrible and disastrous of all wars, civilization itself seeming to be in the balance. But the right is more precious than peace, and we shall fight for the things which we have always carried nearest our hearts—for democracy, for the right of those who submit to authority to have a voice in their own governments, for the rights and liberties of small nations, for a universal dominion of right by such a concert of free peoples as shall bring peace and safety to all nations and make the world itself at last free.

To such a task we can dedicate our lives and our fortunes, everything that we are and everything that we have, with the pride of those who know that the day has come when America is privileged to spend her blood and her might for the principles that gave her birth and happiness and the peace which she has treasured. God helping her, she can do no other.

Wilson, Woodrow. "Making the World 'Safe for Democracy': Woodrow Wilson Asks for War." Sixty-Fifth Congress, 1 Session, Senate Document No. 5 (1917): historymatters.gmu.edu/d/4943/

Preparing to Write

Choose an interesting American state or territory you would like to know more about.

A research report gives facts about a topic rather than the opinion of the writer. A good report is a summary of true statements. The writer gathers facts from an encyclopedia, dictionary, or other nonfiction source and puts them in his own words.

Write about a state or territory. Select some of the following main ideas to write about: history, flora, fauna, land, climate, famous people, sports, or attractions.

These steps will help you prepare to write your research report.

1. Choose the state or territory you will write about.

2. Decide on three to five main ideas that you want to write about.

I would like to write a research report about _____.
(state or territory)

Main ideas	What I already know	What I want to know

Using Notes on Index Cards

Resources in Michigan

1. Natural gas and oil: fuel sources
2. Wind: renewable energy source
3. People: work in manufacturing, agriculture, and tourism

Book Title, pages 10, 15

Resources in Michigan

1. Great Lakes, rivers, inland lakes: fishing for bass, pike, and salmon; recreation; drinking water; irrigation for farming
2. Forests: wood for lumber
3. Wildlife: hunting deer, wild turkey, pheasant, and quail

Book Title, pages 2, 4

I. Resources in Michigan

A. Great Lakes, rivers, inland lakes: fishing for bass, pike, and salmon; recreation; drinking water; irrigation for farming

B. Forests: wood for lumber

C. Wildlife: hunting deer, wild turkey, pheasant, and quail

D. Energy sources: natural gas, oil, and wind

E. _____

Compare the index cards and the outline to answer the questions.

1. What is the total number of main ideas on both index cards together? _____

2. Which main ideas from one index card are combined under one main idea in the outline?

   _____

3. Which main idea from one index card is not used in the outline? _____

4. Add the missing main idea and its details to the outline.

5. How many main ideas are listed in the outline? _____

Research Sources

Keeping a record of the sources you use is both helpful and important when writing a report. Use the cards below to record information from the sources you use for your Research Report. If some information, such as an author's name, is not available, it is acceptable to leave it out. If you consult additional sources and need more cards, record the information on index cards as needed. You will use these cards again later as you write a bibliography. A bibliography is a list of sources used to write a report.

Put a check mark by the type of source that is used. Record the necessary and available information.

Source _____ book   _____ magazine

Author(s) _____

Title of source _____

Title of article _____

Publisher _____

City of publication _____

Date of publication _____

_____ encyclopedia

Editor(s) _____

Edition number _____

Volume number _____

Page number(s) _____

Source _____ book   _____ magazine

Author(s) _____

Title of source _____

Title of article _____

Publisher _____

City of publication _____

Date of publication _____

_____ encyclopedia

Editor(s) _____

Edition number _____

Volume number _____

Page number(s) _____

Internet source

Author(s) _____

Editor(s) _____

Title of source (website) _____

Title of article _____

Page number(s) _____

Publisher _____

Date of publication _____

Date accessed _____

URL address (optional) _____

Internet source

Author(s) _____

Editor(s) _____

Title of source (website) _____

Title of article _____

Page number(s) _____

Publisher _____

Date of publication _____

Date accessed _____

URL address (optional) _____

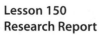

Writing an Outline

Use index cards to write a main point (main idea) beside each Roman numeral.
Use index cards to write supporting details for each main point.

I. _____
    A. _____
    B. _____
    C. _____

II. _____
    A. _____
    B. _____
    C. _____

III. _____
    A. _____
    B. _____
    C. _____

IV. _____
    A. _____
    B. _____
    C. _____

Sample Outline

I. Geography of ____
  A.
  B.
  C.

II. Climate in ____
  A.
  B.
  C.

III. Main religions in ____
  A.
  B.
  C.

IV. Interesting customs and holidays in ____
  A.
  B.
  C.

Sample Research Report

Each paragraph in a research report begins with a topic sentence that states the main idea. The topic sentence is a clue to what the paragraph is about. The other sentences in the paragraph give details that support the main idea.

The sample index cards below were used to develop the first point of the outline with supporting details. Notice how the first paragraph of the report was developed from the outline.

Ireland's geography

1. green rolling hills
2. country is an island
3. Cliffs of Moher—famous; 700 feet
4. rugged mountains around plains

Ireland's Beauty, page 13

Ireland's geography

1. island country
2. a little larger than West Virginia
3. Cliffs of Moher by the Atlantic Ocean
4. has beautiful, lush, green landscape and rolling farmlands, and mountains

The World Encyclopedia, Vol. 10, page 416

I. Ireland's geography

   A. Landscape: Ireland has green rolling hills.

   B. Shape: Ireland is an island.

   C. Size: Ireland is slightly larger than West Virginia in the United States.

   D. Shore: Ireland's western shoreline includes the 700-foot-high Cliffs of Moher by the Atlantic Ocean.

HERITAGE STUDIES

Read the research report. Underline the topic sentence in each paragraph.

Ireland: The Island Country

Ireland's geography includes green, rolling hills and rugged mountains. It is a beautiful place for tourists to visit. Ireland is an island and is slightly larger than the state of West Virginia. The grand Cliffs of Moher on the western coast drop seven hundred feet into the Atlantic Ocean.

Ireland's climate is mild. The winter season is cold and very wet. There is frequent rain and snowfall. The summer season is also wet, but warm. Ireland's skies are mostly cloudy throughout the year, and winds blow off the Atlantic Ocean daily.

There are several religions in Ireland today. Legends say that Saint Patrick was the first person to bring Christianity to Ireland in AD 432. The largest religion in Ireland is Roman Catholicism, and the second largest is Protestant Presbyterianism.

The people of Ireland enjoy many traditional customs and holidays. At Christmas, the Irish display lighted candles in their windows to welcome the Holy Family. One popular holiday is Saint Patrick's Day. Modern Irish people have festivals and plays to honor the memory of Saint Patrick. According to legend, he used a three-leafed shamrock to explain the Trinity. Another legend says he drove snakes from the land.

Writing the Research Report

Use your outline to write the first draft of your research report.

Remember to skip lines in your draft so that you will have space to revise and make proofreading changes.

Write a topic sentence for each paragraph that tells the main idea of that paragraph. Use the details from your outline to write sentences that tell about the main idea.

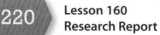

Revising the Research Report

Follow these steps as you continue to work on your research report:

1. Make revisions to your report after checking the content. Combine or delete sentences, reorganize sentences, or add sentences with more information.

2. Make proofreading changes to your report by checking capitalization, grammar, punctuation, and spelling.

Revise your report using the Revising Checklist. Use proofreading marks to make your changes.

Revising Checklist

☐ 1. Each paragraph is about one main idea.

☐ 2. All of the sentences in each paragraph tell about its main idea.

☐ 3. I use words correctly to make my message clear.

☐ 4. All of my sentences tell facts.

☐ 5. I included enough details.

☐ 6. I combined sentences to add more variety.

Proofreading Marks

∧∨   **Add**

‿   **Delete**

≡   **Capital letter**

/   **Lowercase**

○►   **Move**

Ireland: The Island Country

rolling

Ireland has green hills and rugged mountains. It is

tourists   Ireland

a beautiful place for ~~turists~~ to visit. ~~This country~~ is an

and

island. ~~It~~ is slightly larger than the state of west Virginia.

grand

The ~~big~~ Cliffs of Moher on the western coast drop seven

hundred feet into the Atlantic ocean.

Ireland's climate is mild. The winter season is cold

There is frequent rain and snowfall.

and very wet. ~~It rains and snows a lot. I would not like to~~

~~visit Ireland in the winter!~~ The summer season is also wet.

Writing the Bibliography

A bibliography is a list of all the sources used to write a report. The bibliography tells where the information for the report was found. This information usually includes the author, the title of the source, the publication location, the publisher, the date of publication, and the type of source. Your bibliography may include encyclopedias, books, magazines, and Internet sources. The information about these sources is presented in standard formats.

Basic format for a book

Last name, first name of author. <u>Title of book</u>. City of publication: Publisher, Year of publication. Print.

Beam, Ira. <u>Irish Holidays</u>. San Diego: Agar Press, 2002. Print.

Basic format for an encyclopedia

Last name, first name of author. "Title of article." <u>Title of encyclopedia</u>. First and last name of editor (with Ed. in front of the first name). Edition number. Volume number. City of publication: Publisher, Year of publication. Print.

Fowler, Dale. "Ireland." <u>The Travel Encyclopedia</u>. Ed. Michelle Townsend. 3rd ed. Vol. 8. Albany: Children's Press, 1999. Print.

Basic format for a magazine article

Last name, first name of author. "Title of article." <u>Title of magazine</u> Date of publication (Day Month Year): Page number(s). Print.

O'Shea, Leigh. "Christmas in Ireland." <u>Travel the World</u> 5 May 2015: 20–22. Print.

Basic format for an Internet article

Last name, first name of author. "Title of article." <u>Title of source</u>. Publisher, Year of publication. Web. Date accessed (Day Month Year).

Smith, Michael. "A Glimpse of Ireland." <u>Irish Travels</u>. Clover: 2014. Web. 2 Aug. 2015.

Writing the Bibliography

Use your completed research source cards and the sample formats to write a bibliography for your report.

sources listed in alphabetical order by last name or by title

city of publication

Bibliography

Beam, Ira. Irish Holidays. San Diego: Agar Press, 2002. Print.

title of source

Fowler, Dale. "Ireland." The Travel Encyclopedia. Ed. Michelle Townsend. 3rd ed. Vol. 8. Albany: Children's Press, 1999. Print.

O'Shea, Leigh. "Christmas in Ireland." Travel the World 5 May 2015: 20-22. Print.

Smith, Michael. "A Glimpse of Ireland." Irish Travels. Clover: 2014. Web. 2 Aug. 2015.

date of publication

date accessed

medium of publication tells how the information was accessed

Photo Credits

Chapter 1
1 David Lyons / Alamy Stock Photo; 8 Photodisc/Thinkstock

Chapter 2
13 © travispickle - Fotolia.com; 14 DEA PICTURE LIBRARY/De Agostini Picture Library/Getty Images; 19 National Archives; 20 "Carpetbag" by Sobebunny/Wikipedia/CC By-SA 3.0

Chapter 3
25 David Ball/Alamy Stock Photo; 31 "Rawding family sod house" by Solomon D. Butcher/Wikimedia Commons/Public Domain

Chapter 4
37 Photos.com/Thinkstock

Chapter 5
47 Library of Congress, LC-DIG-det-4a05650; 48 NiKreative / Alamy Stock Photo; 49tl "Baud museum mg 8568" by Rama/Wikimedia Commons/CC By-SA 2.0 FR; 49tc, br Science and Society / SuperStock; 49tr "Oliver typewriter 1895"/Wikimedia Commons/ CC By-SA 3.0; 49bl Print Collector/Hulton Archive/Getty Images; 52 "Winslow Homer - Breezing Up (A Fair Wind) - Google Art Project"/Wikipedia/Public Domain; 53 "Buffalo Bill Cody by Sarony, c1880"/Wikimedia Commons/Public Domain; 54 "Jane Addams cph.3a01940"/Wikimedia Commons/Public Domain

Chapter 6
59t "USS Maine Mast Memorial" by Cliff/Wikimedia Commons/ CC By-SA 2.0; 59b "wreck of the USS Maine - low tide - Havana Harbor Cuba - 1911" by Tim Evanson/Flickr/CC By-SA 2.0; 62 © Aleksandar Todorovic | Dreamstime.com; 66l "USAF seal"/Wikimedia Commons/Public Domain; 66ct "United States Department of the Army Seal"/U.S. Dept. of Defense/Wikipedia/Public Domain; 66cb "US-DeptOfNavy-Seal"/U.S. Government/Wikipedia/Public Domain; 66rt "US-MarineCorps-Seal"/U.S. Government/Wikimedia Commons/Public Domain; 66rb "USCG S W"/U.S. Coast Guard/Wikimedia Commons/Public Domain; 68 Library of Congress, LC-DIG-det-4a24807

Chapter 7
71 © Walter Arce | Dreamstime.com; 77l "T Roosevelt" by Pach Brothers/Wikimedia Commons/Public Domain; 77c "William Howard Taft"/Wikimedia Commons/Public Domain; 77r "Woodrow Wilson-H&E"/Wikimedia Commons/Public Domain; 80 "Young Hunters of the Lake"/Cupples and Leon/Wikimedia Commons/Public Domain

Chapter 8
83 "Liberty Memorial 2008" by Charvex/Wikipedia/Public Domain; 84 National Archives; 91 Library of Congress; 92 © havana1234 - Fotolia.com; 93 "102d Aero Squadron - Formation" by Air Service, United States Army/Wikimedia Commons/Public Domain; 94 "William Orpen - The Signing of Peace in the Hall of Mirrors, Versailles"/Wikipedia/Public Domain

Chapter 9
97l "Henry Ford Estate" by Ryan Schreiber/Flickr/CC By 2.0; 97r "A-line1913"/Wikimedia Commons/Public Domain; 99 © Ken Backer | Dreamstime.com; 100 "Charles Lindbergh and the Spirit of Saint Louis (Crisco restoration, with wings)"/Wikimedia Commons/Public Domain; 102 Manuscript Division/Library of Congress/Public Domain

Chapter 10
107t Everett Collection / SuperStock; 107b "Oregon and Transcontinental stock"/Wikimedia Commons/Public Domain; 109 Jupiterimages/Creatas/Thinkstock

Chapter 11
117 Stocktrek Images/Thinkstock; 118 Hulton Archive/Stringer/ Getty Images; 120 Library of Congress; 121 Time Life Pictures/ Contributor/The LIFE Picture Collection/Getty Images; 122 "TBDs on USS Enterprise (CV-6) during Battle of Midway"/U.S. Navy/ Wikimedia Commons/Public Domain; 124 "WHERE OUR MEN ARE FIGHTING OUR FOOD IS FIGHTING"/University of Texas/ Public Domain; 125 "NormandySupply edit"/Wikimedia Commons/Public Domain; 126 © Sylrega | Dreamstime.com; 128 © Ankevanwyk | Dreamstime.com

Chapter 12
131 ©iStockphoto.com/PEDRE; 132 ©Filtv | Dreamstime.com; 134 ShaneGross/iStock/Thinkstock; 135 ©iStockphoto.com/gm-nicholas; 136 ©iStockphoto.com/catnap72; 139 ©iStockphoto.com /EyeJoy

Chapter 13
143 "US and Confederate Flags @ Fort Sumter" by Navin75/Flickr/ CC By-SA 2.0; 144 Pat Canova/Alamy Stock Photo; 146 bren64/ Bigstock.com; 152lt ©iStockphoto.com/JillLang; 152rt Library of Congress, LC-DIG-det-4a08871; 152lct "FortSumter2009" by Bubba73/Wikimedia Commons/CC By-SA 3.0; 152rct © Sborisov | Dreamstime.com; 152lcb "Martin Luther King Jr NYWTS" by Dick DeMarsico/Wikimedia Commons/Public Domain; 152rcb ©iStockphoto.com/Lauri Patterson; 152lb © Heatherc123 | Dreamstime. com; 152rb ©iStockphoto.com/benkrut; 154 ©iStockphoto.com/ sebatl

Chapter 14
157 ©iStockphoto.com/iofoto; 160 louella283/Bigstock.com; 165 © Christopher Eng-wong | Dreamstime.com; 166 ©iStockphoto.com/ Erickson Photography

Chapter 15
169 ©iStockphoto.com/IlexImage; 171tl " hakoar - Fotolia.com; 171tc chloe7992/Shutterstock.com; 171tr C GARVIN/Bigstock .com; 171bl © Crystal Venters | Dreamstime.com; 171bc © Steven Love - Fotolia.com; 171br © Krzysztof Wiktor – Fotolia.com; 174 ©iStockphoto.com/Art Wager; 175 ©iStockphoto.com/tonda

Chapter 16
179 Top Photo Group/Thinkstock; 180 ©iStockphoto.com/Duncan Gilbert; 181 © donyanedomam/123RF; 182 National Park Service/ Jim Peaco; 185 "Rocky Mountain National Park entrance sign IMG 5252.JPG" by Billy Hathorn/Wikimedia Commons/CC By-SA 3.0, GFDL; 186 ©iStockphoto.com/pick-uppath

Chapter 17
189 "MSH82 st helens plume from harrys ridge 05-19-82" by Lyn Topinka/USGS/Wikimedia Commons/Public Domain; 191tl ©iStockphoto.com/jimkruger; 191tr Sami Sarkis / Media Bakery; 191bl © Konrad Reszka – Fotolia.com; 191br ©iStockphoto.com/ Jeff McGraw; 194 ©iStockphoto.com/ssuni

Chapter 18
199 U.S. Navy photo by Petty Officer 2nd Class John F. Looney; 201 ©iStockphoto.com/ziggy_mars; 204 ©iStockphoto.com /dsischo; 205 "PagoPago Harbor NPS" by Tavita Togia/NPS/Wikimedia Commons/Public Domain

All maps from Map Resources